# JUMP

Tiffany Noelle Chacon

WRITE HORSE

*Publishing*

# Dedication

*For my mom: the truest horsewoman I know.*

# Off Course, JUMP #0.5

Click here to download a FREE prequel novella in the JUMP series:

**OFF COURSE: A NOVELLA**

Scan the QR code or go to
the link below to download
the FREE prequel novella for
the JUMP series:

tinyurl.com/offcoursebook

# Contents

# Glossary of Horse Terms

B roken line—two or more show jumping obstacles jumped in succession that are not in a straight line

Colic—severe abdominal pain which can be life-threatening depending on the cause and severity. Colic is the number one killer of horses.

Clean—to jump over an obstacle without knocking it down. A "clean" round in a show jumping competition means that you completed the round without any faults.

Chip in—to add an extra stride or half-stride before going over an obstacle

Fetlock—a part of a horse's leg, above and behind the hoof

Forelock—the top foremost part of a horse's mane, essentially its "bangs"

Girth—a piece of tack that goes under the horse's belly to keep the saddle in place

Grand Prix—the highest level of competition for show jumping, with obstacle heights of up to five foot three inches

Hack/flat—to exercise a horse without jumping them

In-and-out—two show jumping obstacles back-to-back with only one or two strides in between

Jump-off—the second, shorter round in a show jumping competition. The riders who went "clean" in the first round can advance to the jump off. The fastest, clean time wins the event.

Oxer—a show jumping obstacle made of two (or more) poles spread a distance from each other to give the jump width

Rollback—a tight turn from one jump to another

School—to exercise or warm up a horse

Standards—the part of a show jumping obstacle that holds the poles in place. Can be plain or decorative.

Tack—the equipment used to ride a horse. Consists of saddle, bridle, etc. Also a verb—"to tack up" means to put your tack or equipment on your horse.

Triple combination—three show jumping obstacles back-to-back-to-back with only one or two strides in between

Vertical—a show jumping obstacle with poles on top of one another to give it height without the spread or width

# JUMP the Playlist

**JUMP THE NOVEL PLAYLIST:**

Scan the QR code or go
to the link below to listen
to the songs mentioned
in the novel.

https://tinyurl.com/jumpthe
novel

# Chapter One

---

# Free Fall

Cyrus's hooves jolt to the ground as we clear the oxer. The second we land, I grasp my left rein, tugging us into a rollback. We gallop toward a vertical that's got to be taller than me, and it's in this moment that I realize it's the first time since The Breakup that I'm not thinking about It.

Then, of course, once I realize this, I'm thinking about It again. I promptly lose the distance to the vertical, we chip in, and knock down the rail.

"Focus, Mila!" Trina calls from the center of the ring.

This woman. It's like she can read my mind, every time.

Seven frantic strides pass from the vertical to an in-and-out combination as I try to gather my reins and get Cyrus under control. For a moment, an image flashes through my mind of Cyrus and me crashing through the jump; I'm flying headfirst into the ground. I can see my body lying on the ground, forever unmoving. A shudder runs through me as I push Cyrus on toward the in-and-out.

We leave long on the first jump of the set and I grit my teeth together, certain we are going to smash through the next one. Instead, we canter one stride in between and then soar out of the combination, clean. I let out a shaky breath.

I slow Cyrus to a walk, patting his neck. "Good boy," I murmur as adrenaline shivers down my spine. Cyrus pulls the reins out of my hands, the rough leather scorching my palms as it races through my fingers. He stretches his long, dappled gray neck toward the ground—a frequent gesture of his once he finishes a course.

Trina strides over, her short legs making quick work of the sand arena, her bleach blonde hair glinting in the afternoon sun. She's one of the trainers at Zen Elite Equestrian Center, where I board Cyrus and take lessons. And, despite our ten-plus year age gap, Trina's one of my closest friends. Especially after everything that happened with Anya.

"Alright, so the course started out beautifully with this line right here"—she points to a bright blue vertical with a row of multicolored faux flowers resting beneath it, and then five strides to a giant oxer—"that was perfection. The first combo was smooth, but then you lost your concentration after that tight turn." She fixes me with a look like I'm a toddler caught with a spoon in a jar of Nutella. "You're here to forget, Mila. So, forget. And focus on Cyrus, the jumps, the sand, anything but Michael. Feel me?"

I force a laugh, but even as it escapes my mouth, the sound is bitter on my tongue. I'd prefer if no one else in the world knew about my pain, except maybe Cyrus. And the fact that the whole barn knows about it is the literal worst.

"Last thing's last," Trina continues, "but let's just pretend you rode clean and made it to the jump off."

I nod as she points out a shorter course, and then I heel Cyrus into a canter. We start off with a single vertical, then a wide turn to a triple combination.

"More leg!"

I dig my heels into Cyrus, and he responds with a flick of his tail and picks up his pace. We sail through the combination, and I barely have time to imagine falling off. All I can think about is Cyrus's powerful body, bunching and elongating beneath me as we rocket around the course.

Every movement is instinct; Cyrus and me are one. We are flying. We are beyond this earth, somewhere in a different dimension where all I can feel is the wind in my face, the horse connected to me, the reins in my fingers. I'm not even sure I'm breathing.

We pivot back to the oxer we knocked down in the first round, and I sit back slightly to adjust our distance. Cyrus responds perfectly to me and it's heavenly as we glide over the massive jump. A momentary free fall where it's just me and Cyrus, Cyrus and me. Nothing in the world matters.

His hooves hit the sand, and we bounce back to Earth. My calves press against him to urge him on to the next jumps, but he doesn't need it. He's going, no matter what.

We gallop around the ring, clearing every jump with ease. The jump off ends with a skinny vertical that I swear Cyrus has to suck in his belly to get through. We sail over it, and I smile.

We pull up and I release the reins so Cyrus can put his head down. He snorts at the ground gratefully and I can't help but laugh at him. I pat his neck, sticky with sweat, and have to wipe my hands on my breeches before taking the reins again.

Trina's clapping as she walks over to us. "Excellent." She beams. "Really excellent, you two." She pulls a mint out of her pocket and gives it to Cyrus, whose ears perk at the sound of the wrapper. "Look around, Mila. Look at these heights."

I glance at the gigantic jumps Trina set for our practice, and there's an overwhelming moment where I realize that we *had* cleared all of them—and done it really well, too. *This is it*, I let myself think for just a second. *This is everything I've wanted.*

Suddenly, the thought turns sour as I think about Anya. How she should be here. And only a year ago, she *was* here, jumping these same jumps, on this very horse. She'd gotten everything she'd wanted, until fate took it all away.

"You're ready," Trina says. "If you want to move up, you could try the open jumper meter forty class next weekend."

It takes me a minute to understand what she's saying. "Move up?"

The Winter Equestrian Festival, more commonly known as WEF, is starting next weekend. This practice is supposed to be our last before we start the months-long event, with horse shows every weekend. Last season, I was in the Low Amateur Jumper division—with obstacle heights up to 4'6"—but that was before Anya's accident. Before I acquired Cyrus, my sister's Grand Prix horse. I look around at the jumps to confirm that we're jumping *way* above my normal heights. These jumps are Grand Prix level. Trina's saying something, but I'm not quite catching it because I'm trying not to relive Anya's accident in my mind. The image floods my mind—her body collapsing on the ground of the International Arena, Trina and I watching helplessly from the in-gate. I'm yelling her name, running to her. But there's nothing I can do.

"You're one of the most talented young riders I've seen in a long time, and now you've got the horse to go to the top," Trina says, but I see through what she's trying to do—she's saying whatever she thinks I need to hear to get me to let go of my fear of pulling an Anya. And it's not working.

Trina's silently grinning at me, her deeply tanned skin bunching at her cheeks, her eyes squinting expectantly. I shake my head and begin walking Cyrus around the ring to let him cool off and try to catch my breath as dread claws at my chest.

"You're gonna say nothing to that?" Trina says, almost offended.

*Almost* because she knows me, that I'm not trying to offend her. *Almost* because she knows about Anya. *Almost* because she knows 'moving up' means something different to me than to other riders.

"I don't have anything to say," I say truthfully as I fiddle with the buckle on my reins. I close my eyes as Cyrus plods around the arena, each stride jouncing me in the saddle. I tangle my fingers in his mane, needing something to ground me as a panic attack threatens to grab hold of me.

*Breathe, Mila.*

Trina's silent, giving me time to think of something to say.

I don't.

"Well, think about it," Trina says. "You've got the thumbs up from me. You don't have to enter into a Grand Prix quite yet. Just try the meter forty class." She glances at her Rolex, a watch she won at a Grand Prix several years ago on Cyrus's sire, Blue Thunder. "I gotta get ready for my three o'clock, but you consider it." She pauses, glancing up at me. "And

I know from experience that it'll help you forget about Michael. At some point, you've got to make the jump."

"Maybe." *Or*...everything could go back to the way it was, and I'd be perfectly content.

But I don't say that because I don't want to disappoint Trina. She's invested so much in me and Cyrus.

She gives me a stern look, her blonde eyebrow raised, and then waves at me before turning on her heel and leaving the arena. I force myself to focus on my breathing, to think about anything but the jumps, or my memory of Anya's accident.

I lead Cyrus out of the sand ring, passing the open, grassy field we sometimes use for flatting horses. Behind us is the Zen Elite barn with its white concrete and black gabled roof. It's truly a state-of-the-art equine center, complete with a water rehab area for the horses. The farm is dotted with lovely fountains, picturesque gazebos and comfy outdoor furniture to hang out in between rides or to relax and watch whoever's in the ring.

I steer Cy down the barn driveway and out onto the equestrian trails that snake around the equine neighborhood of Wellington, Florida. The trail edges past a canal and turns into a long stretch under shady oaks with Spanish moss dangling in the breeze. I stare up at the trees, the afternoon light filtering down through the branches. A bead of sweat drips from my helmet and streaks down my cheek, almost like a tear. A tear that I refuse to cry, even after so long.

I take a deep breath and a moment later, Cyrus does the same. As if we're feeling the same thing. I lean down and rub his neck. "You're such a good boy," I say. "I'm sorry I'm not ready to move up, and I'm not sure I ever will be." I sigh again. "You deserve better, big guy." He tosses his head, and I can't decide if he agrees with me or not.

Back at home, I scarf down some cold spaghetti Mom left out with a note that says, 'Your sister misses you, please come hang out with her'—a common occurrence these past few months.

I trudge upstairs and pause outside of Anya's room, listening. Blue light emanates from under the door, and I can tell they're watching something. In the year since Anya's accident, since I moved back from the dorms at the University of Miami, I've become adept at standing outside Anya's door, figuring out what movie she and my mom are watching. Today, it sounds like *Wild Hearts Can't Be Broken*, a longtime favorite of Anya's, but particularly after the accident. It's a bit morbid, in my opinion, and my body gives an involuntary tremor as I turn away from her door.

I tiptoe to my room, not wanting my mom to hear me and call me in. It's one of those things I can't quite explain—I moved back here to be helpful, but over the past few months it became harder and harder to cross that threshold into Anya's room. The days and weeks after the accident, watching my only sister, my best friend, shrivel into a shell of herself was more than I could take.

I suspect it's one of the reasons my dad moved out, although he had plenty of others, judging from his hot new secretary that seems a little...friendly. I swallow down the hard lump in my throat, the one that's there more often than not these days.

I want to text Michael, to vent to him about how hard this is. How I miss diving into my sister's bed and telling her all about my day. How empty I feel coming home to a house petrified by grief. But I can't text him; he's not mine to text anymore.

In my room, I toss my purse on my bed. My room is frozen in time from my 18th birthday, right before I went away to school—the floral bedspread that looks like Vera Bradley threw up all over the mattress; a pegboard of birthday cards, favorite shots from various shows, old high school graduation invites. My vanity still has more makeup brushes on it than I know what to do with. In the corner beside the window sits a desk with rows of expansive bookshelves. My brand new business textbooks for the upcoming semester are stacked neatly beside my laptop. Next to the bookshelves, my high school diploma sits in an elegant frame. It's situated above center, with space for at least two more diplomas underneath. My dad's idea, of course.

Even in high school, I wasn't the type of girl to have a bunch of hot guys or boy bands postered onto my walls. I opted instead for a picture of a gray horse in the sun, his mane blowing in the breeze. It's one of those cliché stock photos that had nonetheless beckoned me. Ironically, the horse looks a lot like Cyrus, though my mom and I purchased the picture long before Cy entered our lives.

On the far wall opposite my bed are more personal pictures—one of Anya and me dressed up in our white breeches and black coats, ready to ride in a Sunday classic; another of our family on a Fourth of July yacht ride with Dad's company; and a magazine cover of one of Trina's big wins with Blue Thunder from back in the day. In the shot, Blue is coming down off a huge oxer, his front legs straight as he heads toward the ground, his hind legs still arching over the jump. Trina's face is tight with concentration, and I can almost see the moment they hit the sand, charging through the timer—clean. Her arm raised in jubilee, the crowd cheering with her.

A small tug on my heart reminds me that that could be *me*. On Cyrus. This season. If I want it, which I don't. Not after Anya.

Again the image comes—uncalled—to mind. The sprawling International Arena at WEF. Cyrus, riderless, his reins tossed over his head. Anya's stirrups flapping, empty. The jump behind him, crushed as if King Kong just smashed through it. Anya, on the ground. Never to move below the neck again.

I shake my head, attempting to clear the image. When it doesn't budge, I move toward my laptop and open it, looking for distraction. I pull up a Word document and scroll through my graduate school application essay. The topic? Describe a challenging situation in your life and how you overcame it. Classic.

My challenge? How to *not* write about what happened with Anya. Because I definitely haven't overcome it. Not even close.

I glance through what I've written, about our lives before my dad's success with ViaTech. How the four of us lived in a studio apartment after we immigrated from Ukraine. Each night we would share a few Cups of Noodles for dinner, thanking God for the one dollar ramen and praying for the American Dream. But that wasn't necessarily my challenge to overcome. Sure, we'd had to endure some things—like hunger, for instance, when my parents didn't realize we could get free breakfast *and* lunch at school—but I wasn't sure how to make it mine. It's true that being hungry can make you more hardworking than anyone else around you—because once you've experienced true hunger, you never want to feel that way again. It kept Anya and me focused on school. We weren't the kids who had lots of friends and did tons of extracurricular activities. No, we were the studious but distant ones whose primary friends were each other. Until moving into the dorms at UM, I'd never had a sleepover. In a way, I still hadn't.

My phone buzzes in my pocket.

"Hey, *Tato*," I say to my dad.

"Milochka, how are you?"

"Fine." My boyfriend of two years broke up with me for no apparent reason, my sister is forever crippled, and I pretty much have nothing to say to get me into any reputable graduate program, but yeah, I'm fine. "What's up?"

"Just checking in on those applications. Please tell me you've submitted them."

"I'm working on it right now, actually. This essay just isn't coming together. All the other stuff is done though."

"Do I need to have Natasha write your essay for you?"

"Dad, that's totally unethical."

"I'm just being pragmatic, Milochka. Send Natasha what you have and I'll have her flesh it out a bit. Think of it as...involved editing."

"Sure," I say, even though I know I'm not going to do that.

"Anything else going on I should know about? How's your sister?"

I run my hands against the smooth metal of my laptop, considering how to answer truthfully. "She's alright, watching *Wild Hearts Can't Be Broken* with mom."

A loud exhale blurs the line. "Why does she torture herself like that? And why does your mother let her do that?" He speaks in Ukrainian, which he unknowingly swaps into whenever he's upset.

Even though I'd had the exact same thought earlier, I defend her. "She should be able to choose whatever movie she wants to watch." If fate sentenced her to a life in bed, she should be able to torture herself however she wants, right?

My dad mutters under his breath, some old Ukrainian idiom that I'm not familiar with. "Okay, well keep me updated on those applications. You should get them in this weekend, Mila."

I bristle when he calls me Mila—he only uses that name when he's upset. The diminutive, cutesy Ukrainian version, Milochka, is his typical go-to. "Sure, *Tato*."

We hang up, and instead of working on my application essay, I shut my laptop defiantly and hop in the shower. I listen to my Breakup playlist, belting the lines from Ashe and Niall Horan's song "Moral of the Story." When the song ends, I reach out of the shower and replay it. As I sing along, I want to tell Ashe I'm in pain *and* still in love. The problem is, I don't want to *not* be in love—I just want to be out of pain. When Ariana Grande's "thank u, next" comes on, I try to muster her confidence, and fail.

Out of the shower, I pull up *National Velvet* for the zillionth time. As I watch a young Elizabeth Taylor pretending to gallop down the pathway to her house, I scroll through my text thread with Michael.

All of our texts are pre-Breakup. Lovely texts, sweet texts. Rest-of-my-life texts.

Just last week he'd sent me a picture of the sunset at the barn and said: *Wish you were here with me, you'd make the view 10000x better.*

I don't get it. We had everything—everything a couple could possibly want—and he just threw it away with both hands as if it were nothing. I text my best friend and old dorm roomie, Monica: *I need you to make sure I don't text Michael right now.*

I open my photos and flip through shots from the early days of our relationship. There's a blurry one from Kickback Tavern, our barn's go-to Sunday night restaurant haunt. Michael and me with our faces smooshed together, a cover band somewhere in the background. One at WEF with Michael's bay horse, Khan, in between us. I pause at a photo of us on my birthday last year when Michael took me on a helicopter ride and then dinner at a rooftop terrace with a private chef. It was incredible, one of the best nights of my life, until the very end of the night when it was soured by a shocking revelation that I can't even bring myself to think about. But when I look at the picture, with Michael in his slick Tom Ford suit and me in Anya's hot pink Monique Lhuillier dress, it's like nothing bad ever happened that night. Isn't that funny, how memories can either grow in their bitterness, or all the bad things slough off until you're left with a hazy, happy memory where nothing went wrong?

The nostalgia builds until I open up my text thread with Michael (of course Monica hasn't texted me back, so what else am I supposed to do?) and start to text him. First, an *I miss you*—but that feels too desperate, so I erase it. Then, just a *hey* but that's too nonchalant. I type and subsequently erase several more options, ranging from over-sharing (a long diatribe about my day) to sappy (*I've only ever loved you*) to petty (*Hey Greg! Had so much fun with you last night. Looking forward to Friday.* ). Next I went with humorous: *Booty call??*

I'm laughing at myself as I erase that option when the three dots pop up that indicate Michael is typing something. I sit up quickly, gripping the phone in my hand, my eyes wide as I watch the dots appear, then disappear. My heart hammers against my chest, threatening to force its way through. I scramble for the remote, pausing the movie.

This needs my full attention.

Was he missing me, too? Did he regret The Breakup?

I watch the text thread so closely, I'm sure Michael can feel me staring through the screen.

"C'mon, c'mon, c'mon," I mumble, shaking my phone.

I shake the phone so hard, the 'redo typing' message pops up—except I think it says, 'undo typing.' With tremoring hands, I click the 'redo' button—which I *think* is the 'undo' button—and my previous *Booty call??* text comes back onto the screen. In my haste to re-erase it, I click send.

"NO! NO! NO!" I scream at my phone while I try in vain to undo the message, managing instead to heart the text. I fumble with my phone, trying to fix my mistake, but there's nothing I can do except un-heart the message. I stare at it, gaping at the screen, my pulse is so hard and fast, it feels like my carotid artery might strangle me. In an outburst of frustration, I throw my phone to the floor and pace around my room, raking my hands through my hair as I try to figure out what in the world I can do.

The panic I feel is suffocating. My chest is tight with fear for what seems like the fifteenth time that day. When will it end? When will I feel like a normal person again? I want so badly to cry—to just let it all out—but the tears don't come, and that only makes me more distraught. Like I'm stuck behind the walls of my emotions and they won't let me out.

This isn't the sort of text a girl like me would send. Not in a million years, not if someone held a gun to my head and told me to send this text. (Okay, *maybe* in that particular instance I would send the text. But you get the idea.)

I know I need to figure out a solution. Do I call him and tell him it was a joke? That I didn't mean to send it? Or does that just make me look more desperate?

What if he responds with mockery or vitriol? I would die. I would literally melt into a puddle of steaming hot liquid embarrassment and cease to exist from sheer shame.

My heart does a double-beat as I think of another option: what if he responds positively to my ridiculous text? And that somehow leads to us getting back together?

My hands shake with the idea. I clamber to my phone and pick it up. No response.

"Ugh!" I shake the phone again, and of course the 'undo typing' message pops up and I scream at my phone again. "Stop! Stop!"

In utter defeat, I turn off my phone and climb in bed, too agitated to watch *National Velvet* anymore. With limited options, I get back out of bed and go through a body weight cardio circuit—jumping jacks, burpees, mountain climbers. Then three minute-long planks, counting to myself, until my arms and core are quivering.

I hide under my obnoxiously cheerful quilt and turn my phone back on, daring to peek at the text thread with Michael again, but there's nothing except a text from Monica: *Stay strong, Mila!* along with a GIF of a female bodybuilder undulating her chest muscles. Any other time, I'd think this was hilarious. But not today. I close my eyes, burying my head in my arms, wondering if I'll need to stay hidden here forever.

Eventually I go back to *National Velvet,* and fall asleep sometime after two in the morning, only to have my normal round of nightmares. Except this time Michael is on the sidelines laughing at me.

# Chapter Two

# A True Horsewoman

Over the next week, I spend more time at the barn than usual, hacking horses that need to be exercised, grooming Cyrus far more than he needs, and generally wasting time waiting for Michael to show up. WEF starts this weekend, so I know he needs to flat his horse at least a few times. I see his black Tacoma once when I'm in the middle of riding, but despite my best efforts, our paths don't cross. I wonder if someone in the barn is tipping him off as to when I'm here or on a horse, and I can't help but evaluate who that might be. Could it be one of the girls? Was he already hooking up with one of them? My mind flashes to Amber and how handsy she was with Michael that one night at Kickback Tavern when she was three sheets gone thanks to a bad mixture of beer, tequila, a Red Bull, and not much to eat at the show. It also could be Colleen, who would flirt with a garden gnome as long as it was facing her way.

I'm fuming about this one afternoon while I tack up a bay mare named Missy. One of the other college students who works at the barn, Alex Caballero, comes over to help. He's about my age, maybe a bit older, and has a way with horses that makes me think he'd been a horse in another life. *Every* horse—old, blind, deaf, ornery—loves Alex. Even Missy, who refused to lift her feet for me to clean, raises her hoof for Alex with only a gentle touch of her fetlock.

Alex has been at the barn as long as I have, maybe even longer. He was one of a handful of barn people who came to visit Anya in the hospital after her accident, and he brought his mom's guava cheesecake, which was to die for. My parents were convinced he came bearing gifts because he had a crush on Anya, but I'm not so sure about that. In fact, an embarrassing interaction we had before Anya's accident—where he thought I was asking him out—pretty much confirmed my hypothesis that Alex had at least the inkling of a crush on me. Although that was over a year ago, and he's probably dated a ton since then.

Despite that interaction, he always offers me sound advice when asked, in some cases even surpassing Anya's wisdom and insight. *And* he took care of Cyrus in the days and weeks after the accident, which gives him extra bonus points in the good-guy department.

We fall into a comfortable silence as we groom and tack up Missy, like we've done a hundred other times with many different horses. I must be a bit aggressive with the equipment because at one point Alex says, "What did that girth ever do to you?"

I pause, the girth dangling in my hand, and exhale loudly. "Apparently it's easier to take out my frustration on the tack than on someone who won't even show their face around here."

Alex's dark brown eyes settle on me as he takes the girth from my hand. He always makes me a little jittery, the way his gaze lingers on me. Like he's seeing more than I'm showing. Maybe if he weren't so attractive I'd feel less nervous around him. That's what I get for having had only one serious boyfriend in my twenty-one years of life—I don't really know how to act around hot guys. Dating is a muscle that can atrophy, apparently.

"As long as you don't take it out on Missy, you can punish the girth as much as you want," he says with a smile that doesn't quite show his teeth.

"I would never," I say, slightly offended that he'd even allude to me mistreating a horse.

"I know, Mila."

"Do you, though?" And I can't help it, I'm feeling defensive.

He pauses from tightening the girth around Missy. His eyes are on me again, and something in my stomach quivers. Alex is such an interesting juxtaposition—his dark, buzzed hair and wiry, athletic frame make him look like a soldier, and yet he has one of the gentlest dispositions of any man I know.

"Of course I do," he says softly. "You're one of the truest horsewomen I know."

"Oh," I say, because I don't know how to respond to that. His statement makes me feel like springtime—warm and safe. *A true horsewoman.* "Thanks."

Alex shrugs and goes back to tightening the girth, as if he hadn't just told me the nicest thing anyone's said since Anya's accident, or maybe ever. When I keep staring at him, he looks up and gives me another closed-mouth smile, his dark espresso eyes crinkling in the corners.

After I get the bridle on Missy, I lead her out of the barn and Alex gives me a leg-up, his hands solidly gripping my calf as he boosts me onto Missy's back. This sums up Alex, I think: strong, steady, always around to offer a helping hand.

"Thanks, Alex," I say as I settle into the saddle, stretching my legs out before I put them into the stirrups.

"My pleasure, boss." He gives me a two-fingered salute, a frequent gesture of his.

I trot Missy around the ring, turning her in figure-eights and spiraling circles. I'm thinking about Michael, of course—about when he's going to finally show up at the barn, what I'm going to say to him, why he broke up with me.

But then I think about Alex's comment: *one of the truest horsewomen.* A warm feeling spreads through my stomach and I can't help but smile. I like that more than I want to admit, but it also makes me wonder...if I'm so *true,* would I be this hesitant to move up divisions with Cyrus? The thought pings around my head, unsettling as an out-of-control pinball hurtling past the flippers. I want so badly to clamp down on my mind, to just *stop* thinking for one minute. The closest I ever get to truly getting a break from my oppressive mind is when I'm on course. And even that is riddled with fear.

After my ride, as I cool down Missy, Trina comes into the arena for a lesson with Emmy and Ella, twin eleven-year-old girls who show their ponies in a division called Puddle Jumpers. They're unendingly cute, with their matching braids and polka dot saddle pads.

"Thinking about the High Amateur Jumpers?" Trina asks.

I smile flatly at her but don't respond.

"It's Friday in the DeNemethy Arena—one of your favorites."

I roll my eyes and laugh. If I'm going to be jumping a course with obstacles almost as big as me, which arena I'm in won't make one lick of difference. I wave her off and head back to the barn, only to see Michael's truck hightailing it out of the driveway.

On Friday, the first day of the Winter Equestrian Festival, I'm up at 5 a.m. Not because I have to be, but because I'm too excited-slash-nervous to sleep. And of course I can't eat a normal meal before I compete, so I'm making myself a smoothie when my mom comes down the stairs. She's bleary-eyed and her hair's mussed, and for a second I do a double-take because she looks more like Anya than my mom. My mom and Anya both have dark hair, porcelain skin, and blue eyes. The pair of them look like delicate china dolls whereas I take after my dad with his olive skin, light brown waves, and hazel eyes. My mom has always been slender, but in the past year as she's taken care of Anya, she's gotten to the point where she's more skin and bones than anything else, and every time I really look at her, it makes my stomach plummet to my feet. So I just try not to look too hard, because I'm not really sure what else to do.

"You're going to wake up your sister," my mom scream-whispers over the sound of the blender.

*So?* I want to say. She can go back to bed literally any time. She lives there. "Sorry," I mumble instead, and turn off the blender.

"She's having a rough time." My mom sits down at the kitchen table, her oversized long-sleeved shirt pulled over her hands, and she seems very young to me. Too young to have a crippled daughter. "I walked in on her crying so hard last night, her nose was all congested and she couldn't clear it. She could barely breathe." She shakes her head, scrubbing her face with her hands. She's silent for a few moments as if she's reliving what she saw. "She could've suffocated. Oh my gosh, what if she was trying to kill herself?"

The way she's speaking, I can't quite tell if she's talking to me or simply processing out loud. Since Anya's accident, my mom quit her job as a nurse anesthetist and has cared for Anya full-time. It's heartbreaking to watch my mother—my strong, smart, confident mom—become a husk of her old self. I barely know how to interact with her anymore.

Eventually I say, "I think she was just crying, Mom. Wouldn't you be, too?" I put an arm around her and kiss the top of her head. I want to say something—*It'll be alright* or *Anya will get through it*—but I don't. Maybe because I don't believe it, or because I don't think it'll help.

"Can you talk to her, Milochka? She needs you. She needs you even more than she needs me."

This sentiment peppers every conversation my mom and I have. "What can I say that hasn't already been said, Mom?"

She sighs heavily, twisting her hands in her lap. I pull away, unsure of what else to say or do in this moment. After a while, she says, "It's hard to have peace with the birds chirping outside." And I'm not sure if this is one of my mom's infamous weird sayings, or if there are actual birds chirping outside Anya's bedroom.

I tell her I have to go, even though I don't, and head out into the dawn.

At the show, I find myself not at the DeNemethy Arena with the colossal jumps, but at the Mogavero Arena with the very safe-sized jumps. Trina and I wait by the in-gate, memorizing the course posted on the board, waiting to walk the arena to check out the course up close.

In the warm-up ring, horses and riders are going in every direction at top speed. One of the things I love about WEF is that you can often hear people from all over the world talking in different languages, all connecting over one thing: horses. The beauty of this sport is that young and old, men and women, all compete against each other. In my division, there are 60-year-old riders and 18-year-old riders, and we're all competing on the same footing. I soak in the energy of the showgrounds, feeling like I'm a part of something bigger than just myself.

"Getting ready to walk the course over in the Mogavaro," the in-gate keeper's voice booms from a speaker beside us, "then I've got Nancy in first, Jill in one, Tracy in two, Ed in three, Alan in four, Mallory in five."

"You're thirty-sixth in the order," Trina says as we walk into the sand arena.

Typically in show jumping, there are two rounds. The first is an elimination round, meaning that if you have any faults—if you knock down a jump, have a refusal, or go over the time allowed—you don't continue on to the next round. If you go 'clean'—meaning that you don't have any faults—you can proceed to the jump off, which is the second and final round. In this round, the fastest clean time wins.

This particular class that I'm in is called power and speed, which means that instead of having a break in between the first and second round, if you go clean, the second round begins immediately after you jump the final hurdle in the first round. This type of class always makes me a little anxious. I like being able to have a few seconds in between rounds to catch my breath and review the jump off course before getting back to it. But not in this class.

The course begins with an oxer by the in-gate—which is always a little harder for some horses, because when they see the in-gate, they want to go through it, not past it.

"Make sure you get enough pace before you get here, or Cyrus will suck up before the first jump," Trina says as we walk past the yellow and black oxer. There's an eight stride broken line to a tall vertical with standards that have huge butterfly wings exploding from the sides. Then, a wide turn to a jump made of faux bricks.

"I doubt he'll balk at this one, but make sure you push him through just in case." We walk past the jump, counting off the strides to the next obstacle. "You could do this line in six strides if you take a more direct path," Trina says.

The next line is a string of jumps devoted to autism awareness, with colorful puzzle pieces across the standards and multi-colored rails. There's a vertical and then five strides to an in-and-out, which is a two-jump combination back-to-back.

"This combo might be tight for Cyrus, so make sure you're not too hurried through the five strides, or else it's going to get real tight in here real fast."

"You think I could do the line in four strides?"

"Hmm, I wouldn't."

After the in-and-out is a tight turn—a rollback—to a skinny jump and then a long straightaway to a sprawling water jump.

"Keep the momentum through the turn here, and make sure you get him moving to the water, though he probably won't have a problem with that."

It's true. Cyrus can be lazy when we're schooling or flatting, but once he's in the ring, he's as much of a stallion as can be. Which is to say, he's nuts.

After the water jump is an airy vertical that looks like it'll knock down if you blow on it.

"Collect him after the water, or else he's gonna King-Kong right through this thing."

The power portion of the course ends with a turn to a fan jump, where the rails are splayed out on one end of the jump so that it gets gradually wider the farther out you go. The challenge with this jump is that if you don't turn tight enough, you'll be pointed right at the widest part of the jump. It'll be extra challenging with a horse as huge as Cyrus. Before, I would've relished a challenge like this. But now, my heart thuds as I try not to picture Cyrus getting caught on the top rail, the pole stuck between his front legs as we topple to the ground, hind end overhead. I can practically hear the sickening crunch of Cyrus's neck breaking, and then mine not long after. A shudder runs through me, shaking me to my core.

"Mila?"

I return to the course, leaving the image behind as Trina instructs me on the jump off. Once over the fan jump, if we go clean, the speed portion would start immediately. I make a note of where the timers are located. It's a long gallop to the skinny, then a quick turn to a line with another brick wall to an in-and-out. There's an option after the combination to make a *super* tight turn in between two jumps, or go the long way around. You could risk running into the wrong jump if you made the turn too tight, but if you go around, you'd lose quite a few seconds on the clock.

Trina and I discuss the pros and cons of going inside versus outside, but she ultimately leaves the decision up to me. We run through the rest of the jump-off, a couple more tight turns and a rollback to the final vertical. Then I go to the stands to watch the first few riders. I keep looking around for Michael, hoping to spot him somewhere on the showgrounds. He's in a different division, which is at a different time, but that doesn't stop me from looking for him.

The first rider on course is a girl about my age riding a petite chestnut with four white socks, with the look of a Thoroughbred. He speeds around the course like a maniac, knocking down three jumps in the power round. The second horse on course shies at the water jump. He comes almost to a complete standstill in front of it, but decides to jump it anyway. The result is that the rider—who was prepared for her horse to stop—gets left behind while her horse bunny-hops over the water. I stand on shaking legs as I watch her splash into the jump, but she immediately stands up, wiping her gloved hands on her wet breeches. I take a shivering breath and sit back down, trying not to imagine Anya walking out of the ring. I run my hands over my face and busy myself braiding and unbraiding my hair as I continue to watch the next couple of rides.

"I'm on in about twenty," I tell Alex as I walk into the temporary barns to get Cyrus. The barns are basically glorified circus tents—huge, white steepled canvases with rows and rows of stalls underneath that can be assembled and taken apart in a few hours. Thousands of horses gather here in Wellington in the winter to compete, and all of them need a place to stay. The temporary barns are miraculous in a way—one day it's an empty field, the next it's home to all of these horses for four months.

Alex is cleaning a bridle, hands slick with saddle soap, which he quickly wipes on a rag hanging from his front pocket.

"Got it, boss," he says. I cringe when he calls me that, and I wish I had the nerve to tell him not to.

He grabs Cyrus out of the stall and brings him to a makeshift grooming area in one of the stalls. I fix my hair into a hairnet, brushing my hair over my ears and twisting the rest up into my helmet. Then Alex and I orbit each other as we groom and tack up Cyrus.

"You nervous?" Alex asks, as if he can sense it. Maybe that's what makes him so good with the horses; he's got some kind of sixth sense.

I shrug. "It's power and speed, which for whatever reason, I don't like. I prefer to regroup before the jump off—assuming I get there at all. And, I don't know, the jumps always look the biggest the first week of WEF."

He smiles, this time showing his teeth, revealing a slightly crooked incisor I've never noticed before. "You'll do great."

And then we're both staring at each other, a little longer than necessary for polite conversation, and I almost forget what I'm doing. I notice for the first time a smattering of faint freckles across the bridge of his nose, and suddenly I want to run a finger over them. His face is all sharp angles, high cheekbones, and almost-black eyes. The kind a girl could get lost in. Not me, of course, but some girl somewhere.

Cyrus snorts, seeming to remind us of the task at hand. Alex breaks the gaze and settles my saddle on Cyrus's back, deftly hooking the girth on his side before passing it to me. As I cinch the girth, Cyrus's belly puffs out and I poke him in the ribs.

"I know what you're doing, mister," I mutter to him. Cyrus doesn't like his girth tightened, so he pulls this maneuver so it won't be too tight on him—but usually by the time I hoist myself onto the saddle, it's flapping around on his back.

Alex is at Cyrus's head with the bridle, taking off his halter as he murmurs to my horse in Spanish. I don't know exactly what he's saying, except that I hear my name and the word *bueno*.

"Bewitching my horse?" I joke.

Alex smiles again and I wonder why I've never noticed how nice his smile is. "A little hex to help you through to the speed." He winks and my stomach turns a little flip. I shake my head, reminding myself that I'm in love with Michael and don't need to be distracted by hot grooms with nice smiles while I try to win Michael back.

Alex hands me the reins. "I'll give you a leg up."

Then a piercing cry comes from a few aisles over: "INMAGRACIÓN! POLICÍA!"

All of a sudden, there's a tension that swoops into the temporary barns unlike anything I've ever felt before. It's like panic has become a physical force, pressing itself down on every single person in the barns. In front of me, Alex tenses, his knees bent as if he's about to run. The shouting continues, and I try to piece together what's happening even as my brain is shouting at me that something really bad is going down. Cyrus stamps his feet nervously, and I'm gripping his reins so tightly I know that my uneasiness is traveling straight down the leather straps into my perceptive horse.

"What's going on?" I ask, but he doesn't respond. His eyes are wide, glancing around, his fear palpable. I wonder, did Alex do something illegal, and he's fearful of arrest? Surely not *this* Alex. "Alex? What's happening?"

When he still doesn't reply, I reach out and grab his hand. He finally seems to come back to the present and says, "Immigration police." I see him swallow, his throat bobbing. "If they arrest me, they'll send me back to Cuba." Alex is gripping my hand so hard, it's going numb. "My mom will be here alone. She's...sick."

There's a split second of confusion before understanding washes over me—Alex is an illegal immigrant.

"I'll help," I tell him above the shouts and chaos erupting throughout the temporary barns. I hear the immigration officers in the next aisle over, asking for ID and speaking gruffly with the grooms. I grab my backpack, fumbling for the keys, and shove them into Alex's hands. "Get out of here."

His shoulders slump. "They'll think I'm stealing your car. It'll only make it worse."

I stare down at the keys, our hands tangled together. "Right, okay. I'll drive, you can get in the backseat. Hide." I grab a scrim sheet. "We can cover you with this. C'mon." I quickly tie Cyrus up to the cross-ties and take Alex's hand, but right as we're emerging from the grooming stall, a swarm of immigration police barges down our aisle.

Thinking fast, I pull Alex back into the stall, ripping my helmet off as I back myself into a corner. I can't quite find the words to explain my plan, so I simply wrap my hand around his neck and pull him into a kiss.

At first, Alex seems bewildered, and, gentleman that he is, tries to back away. "Trust me," I whisper, and tug at him. I feel his heart beating wildly as he presses closer, accepting the kiss and my attempt to help him.

He smells of saddle soap and hay. There's a fruity taste on his lips, as if he'd recently snagged a few Jolly Ranchers from the show office. I try not to think about what I might taste like—probably the coffee smoothie I guzzled on the way here.

I remember the rag in Alex's pocket and toss it away from us. I wrap my other arm around his back, feeling his muscles tense.

All of the thoughts swirling in my mind—how to help Alex, what immigration would do with him, how this compares to kissing Michael—flee as Alex deepens the kiss, his mouth opening against mine. I can't even think about how good of a kisser he is—there's nothing but this moment, with his mouth against mine, my body crushed between his and the wall. There's no barn, no horses, no immigration police.

It's only us. For a moment.

"Immigration! Show your IDs," a man's voice shouts from the aisle behind us, and I startle. But I also know that sticking with the kiss is the best way of saving Alex. He pulls back slightly, and I murmur against his mouth, "Don't stop," and against every polite bone in my body, we keep kissing, even as Immigration pauses outside the stall.

I pray with all my might they won't call our bluff, that they will feel as uncomfortable as I do and just move on. I can tell by the way Alex's lips stiffen on mine that he's thinking the same thing. I grip his shirt in my fist and pull him even closer, my limbs shaking with the absurdity of this situation.

In my backpack beside us, my phone is going crazy. Surely Trina is calling me, losing her mind that I'm not at the ring yet. In the aisles around us, the turmoil is amping up. Spanish and English converge into indiscernible squabbles. There's a distant sound of a woman crying, along with the typical sounds of horses stamping their feet, snorting and clip-clopping outside the barn.

After what seems like an eternity, the clatter of the immigration police moves on to the next barn. Alex pulls away, his forehead resting on mine, as we pant each other's air.

"It worked," I say, breathless. I'm experiencing an odd mixture of feelings—waves of relief curl through me while pings of electricity bounce around my stomach.

Alex has his arm leaning on the stall wall just above me, and I find myself unintentionally comparing him with Michael. I'm a little on the tall side—5'7"—and Michael is only 5'9", so I rarely feel small with him. But in this moment with Alex, I feel dainty, holdable. And I'd be lying if I said I didn't like it. I imagine for a second what it would be like if Alex wrapped his arm around my waist and kissed me because he *wanted* to, not because he needed to.

Alex shakes his head, and he's clearly not making eye contact with me. "I can't believe it," he says as he backs away, and the cool air that marks our separation seems almost too cold. "Thank you for...that." He waves a hand at the corner, and my face warms as I realize he feels embarrassed. Did he not like the kiss? I suddenly feel panicky, like I need to get out of this corner, stat.

"We need to get you out of here, in case they circle back."

"You'll miss your ride."

We—unwillingly, it seems—make eye contact, and there's something in his eyes I can't quite explain, some emotion I can't put my finger on. Whatever it is, it's not helping the tingling behind my belly button. "There will always be another one," I say, a little too breathlessly. I'm surprised by my own sentiment. I've never missed a show before, for any reason.

"There's a few others like me," Alex says.

"Illegal?"

He cringes at the word. "Sort of, yeah. Bastien and Carlos, they're somewhere on the showgrounds."

"We'll call them once we're in the car, see if we can help."

Alex nods, and we quickly put Cyrus back in his stall, taking off his bridle. I feel as though I've just finished a huge course, the way the adrenaline is quaking through me. I jog to my car and pull it as close to the barn as I can get, looking around for the Immigration police. When it's clear, I flash my brights and Alex darts into the backseat, scrim sheet over his shoulders. We call and manage to get a hold of Carlos, who says Bastien was picked up by Immigration, but Carlos is hiding in a bathroom stall near the Mische Grand Hunter Ring. I drive around the showgrounds and we scoop him up, both guys huddling in the backseat of my tiny BMW.

The showgrounds are in chaos as ICE officers are hauling people away left and right. There's a horse standing in the middle of one of the rider paths, riderless and without anyone holding him, his reins looped around his neck. He's looking around, seemingly wondering what's going on. I want to go to him, find his owner, but I also know I need to get Alex and Carlos out of here.

As we exit the showgrounds, I wave to the stern guard at the gate and speed off down Pierson Road. I exhale, trying to shake off all the tension and chaos built up in my chest. *What just happened?* I look back in my rearview mirror at Alex, who's now sitting up in my backseat, staring out the window. His eyes flicker to mine, meeting in the mirror, and we both quickly look away.

If someone had told me this morning that *this* is how my day would go, I would not have believed them. And yet, here I am, still feeling the tingle of Alex's lips on mine as I drive him far away from the ICE officers wanting to arrest him.

This is *not* at all how I thought this day would go.

# Chapter Three

# Rollback

It turns out I didn't miss my class. After I dropped off Alex and Carlos at Trina's barn, where he said they'd be safe, I turned around and came back to the showgrounds. When I get to the ring, Trina pulls me into a hug—which is very uncharacteristic of her.

"What do you know?" she asks.

"Immigration police, they arrested a ton of people. They took Bastien."

Trina nods grimly, lips pressed into a thin line. "What about Alex?"

"He's safe. I...helped him."

"Oh, thank God." Trina's so visibly relieved that Alex is safe, it makes me wonder what I don't know. Does she know about Alex's mom? I want to ask more, but Trina's telling me about her experience at the ring.

"They shut down the ring for a while—you *know* how rare that is. Unless they're calling an ambulance, that just doesn't happen." She shakes her head, kicking at the ground with her boot. "They took one of the trainers, Esteban, you know him?"

I nod. I've seen him around. He's always wearing a Tommy Hilfiger polo shirt and muddy sneakers.

"Can they do this? Just take people in the middle of the day, in the middle of their work like this?"

Trina shrugs, holding out her hands to encompass the showgrounds. "They just did."

We stare at each other for a moment but eventually she gestures toward Cyrus as if to say, *We might as well get on with the show.*

With shaking hands, I get on Cyrus and start warming up. The practice ring that's connected to the Mogavero is approximately the size of a dime, and navigating around the other horses and riders as they zoom over their practice fences brings out a whole tidal wave of stomach flutters. Trina sets an oxer in the center of the practice jumps and moves it gradually higher each time we clear it.

The in-gate keeper's voice crackles over the speaker: "I've got Andy on deck, Helen in one, Julie in two, and then Mila wrapping up the class. Then we're going to drag and set for our eighteen to thirty-five Adult Jumpers." He pronounces my name like *Mih-lluh* instead of *Mee-lah*, which is just annoying. It only has four letters; it's really not that complicated. Also, has he not ever heard of Mila Kunis? C'mon, man. But I guess that's what you get when your name isn't Andy or Helen or Julie.

I zero in on the fact that the next class after mine is Michael's class. Which means I might see him walk the course after my class. Should I find a reason to walk that course, too? Or hang around the in-gate? All of a sudden I'm thinking about the kiss with Alex, his hands tangled in my hair, the way his full lips felt against mine. Heat floods me, and I push the memory away, reminding myself that I was helping a friend, not starting a relationship.

I slow Cyrus to a walk and review the course in my mind, pointing at each jump with a gloved finger. Trina gives me some last-minute pointers based on the riders she watched while she was waiting for me, but honestly, my nerves are getting the best of me and I don't hear much. I try to visualize Cyrus and me going around the course clean, but in my mind's eye, we crash through every other jump.

When I'm two riders out, Trina changes the oxer into a vertical and sets it ridiculously high. My heart is about to crash out of my chest, but Cyrus is on auto-pilot as we navigate over the jump.

"Nice," Trina says. "Let's do this thing." We walk to the in-gate and I try to take deep breaths, but my lungs won't let me take in too much air.

And then, it's our turn.

Trina gives Cyrus a pat on the rump and says, "Good luck, chica."

We trot into the arena, making sure to pass the water jump so Cyrus can get a good look at it before we start the course.

"Our final rider on course for the Amateur Jumpers," the hoity-toity British announcer's voice reverberates over the ring. "Miss Mila Kozak riding Cyrus Van der Bergh."

Without even pressing my heels into his side, Cyrus bursts into a gallop when the buzzer goes off. He does his obligatory pre-course buck, and I can't help but smile nervously. It's showtime.

I adjust my reins, perching myself up in the stirrups a bit as I steer Cyrus toward the first jump. I sense Trina at the in-gate, her hands clasped in front of her, talking to herself as she watches us like she's done for me and Anya a thousand times before.

We gallop up to the oxer and I hold my breath as we rocket over it. Trina and the in-gate blur away from us and now all I can focus on is the course. Cyrus doesn't balk at the outrageous butterfly jump, and he gives the faux brick fence extra space as we fly over it.

We're going a little fast as we jump into the autism awareness line, so I sit back and rein him in for the five strides to the in-and-out. Trina was right—it is tight, and we chip in a bit at the last jump, but Cyrus twists his hind legs to avoid hitting the rail. We clear it.

I urge Cyrus through the rollback. We're over the skinny and then we're charging at the water. Cyrus's hoof beats are thunderous, his ears pointing forward as we approach. At the last second, I knot my hands into his mane, afraid of being separated from him like I'd seen with the rider earlier, but Cyrus doesn't hesitate one bit as we glide over the expansive jump.

As soon as we land, I'm collecting Cyrus for the airy vertical. He's fighting me a bit, tugging at the reins—he wants to *go*—but eventually I have him under control and our spot is perfect. We get over it with plenty of room to spare, and then I pull him into a tight turn and we're darting over the fan jump, right in the middle of it, and just like that we're onto the speed portion.

I click to Cyrus, pushing him faster; his ears flick back to me, and then forward again as we approach the first jump in the jump off—the skinny. We're going too fast, so I try to pull him up so we don't plow through the jump, and we end up adding an extra stride at the base of the jump and Cyrus has to get what Trina calls "gymnastical" to clear the jump.

We don't have a ton of momentum because of the chip-in by the time we're over the skinny, so I'm heeling him faster as we rollback to a brick jump. We leave long, and it's not pretty; I land on his neck and have to collect myself before we get to the in-and-out. Thankfully it's a long gallop to the combination, and by the time we get there, our pace is on point for the first time in the jump off and we get through the in-and-out with a near-perfect rhythm.

I pull hard on Cyrus's right rein to make the inside turn, and we *almost* hit one of the jumps, but Cyrus does this little hop thing to avoid making contact with the standard. Once we navigate around the turn, we fly through the broken line, making it in four strides instead of Trina's suggested five. Then we're charging at the very last jump—the airy vertical—and I realize we're going way too fast. Cyrus is all strung out, and I'm exhausted from the long course, so even though I'm hauling on him to slow down, it's not enough.

I hear Trina from the in-gate: "Slow down!" But even her shouts are not what we need to manage such a drastic change of pace. Sure enough, we bulldoze through the jump, the top pole hitting Cyrus's legs and catapulting a full stride in front of us. I brace myself for impact, but Cyrus simply hops over the errant pole, and we've finished the course.

Despite a somewhat disastrous last jump, I'm smiling and patting Cyrus's neck. We did it! We finished the power and speed and we didn't crash. I feel jittery, like I just downed five packets of Pop Rocks, and can barely comprehend Trina's feedback as she reviews the course with me. I have a few mints in my pocket, and Trina does too, so we're taking turns feeding them to Cyrus. He nuzzles Trina for one, chomps it down, then turns his head all the way back to me and I lean down to hand him one. He's happy, I'm happy, Trina's moderately happy—except for the last jump.

I'm so pleasantly distracted that I barely notice Michael walking past me as he waits for the tractor to finish dragging the arena so he can walk his course.

"Go get your ribbon," Trina says to me, and I'm surprised to find out that even with the rail, Cyrus and I placed tenth in the class since we had the fastest time of the four-faulters. She holds Cyrus as I jump down and head to the in-gate to collect my white tenth place ribbon. When I turn around, there's Michael, waiting at the gate. I was hoping he'd be looking at me, watching my ride, feeling regret as he observed my happiness. But no, he's standing next to another rider, a girl named Catrina who's barely eighteen, and they're laughing. Flirting. His perfect smile, with those touchable dimples, all on display, not for me but for her. Watching him, I'm cracked open, like an egg with its yoke spilling over jagged shells, all of the happiness of my ride seeping away. It's only been a few weeks, and seeing him like this feels like someone ripped the scab off of a wound. I'm clutching the ribbon so hard, I've cracked the cardboard back. When the announcer declares that the riders can walk the course, I'm left standing by myself, watching Michael walk away from me yet again.

# Chapter Four

---

# Kickback and...Relax?

O n my way home from the show, I'm thoroughly afflicting myself with my Breakup playlist. Wild Rivers' "Thinking 'Bout Love," the acoustic version, has me thinking about the first time Michael said he loved me. It was after a Sunday show in March. The whole barn crew met at Kickback Tavern for dinner like we usually did, and Anya forced everyone onto the dance floor when the cover band played a Ben Rector-esque version of Whitney Houston's "I Wanna Dance With Somebody."

Michael and I had been kind-of, sort-of seeing each other for a few months, but it had gotten more serious during WEF that season, and we had been basically inseparable since January. The barn crew was all clustered together, dancing and shout-singing at the top of our lungs—me loudest of all—and Michael was behind me, wrapping his arms around me and just smiling as he watched me. And, I knew. I knew as sure as my heart was beating and my synapses were firing that he loved me. I was so confident of it that I turned around, threw my arms around his neck, and said, "You love me."

Michael laughed, his blue eyes dancing like the waves, his dimples deepening. "I do."

"What's that?" I said, leaning in playfully.

"I do."

"You do what?"

"I do love you."

I pulled him into a kiss, right there in the middle of everyone at the barn, and a cheer went up around us. Trina shouted something lame like, "Get a room!"

Finally, I tore myself away, gazed up at Michael and said, "I know."

As I think back on that girl, the confident, life-of-the-party Mila, she's so far from the person I am today. I'm a shard of my former self, broken in too many ways, unable to piece myself back together. And it's no wonder Michael couldn't stick it out.

In this moment, I feel Anya's loss so keenly. She would be the one to put me together, to make me move on from Michael, or concoct a plan to get him back. But she's too lost to her own sorrows—and rightly so.

I shut the music off, the ache in my heart resonating in the empty, silent car. Before I can dissolve into a bucket of self-pity on the Turnpike, I call my dad. Not because he'll make me feel better—that's not exactly his strength—but because he'll distract me. Or at least bully me into a different state of mind.

I am my father's daughter, from our light brown waves to our hazel eyes to our apparent self-centered natures. The main way we differ, though: my dad is a bulldozer. And I am decidedly *not*.

I start to tell him about Alex—not the kissing part, but the rest of it. I'm practically yelling into the vacuum of the car and it hits me that it's a little strange I'm so passionate about this. I shake my head, telling myself I'm just being a good person.

"Why are you telling me this, Milochka?" I know he's not being rude; my dad is highly pragmatic and if he doesn't see the point, he says it.

"Is there anything you can do to help?"

"I'm sure there is, but the question is, *why*?"

"He's a good guy."

"There's lots of good guys in the world. Not all of them can get my support."

Now I'm feeling hesitant about bringing it up. Why did I think my dad would want to help?

"He's a...friend," I say with as little confidence as a baby bird staring down a hungry alligator.

"A friend? I see. Look, Milochka, I've got a lot going on. We've got this merger we're overseeing, I don't have time for anything except helping you get your applications in."

I bypass the application remark and try for a different angle: "*Tato*, c'mon, I'm surprised you don't want to pay it forward after what we've been through—"

"Pay it forward? Mila, I came into this country *legally*, I did my due diligence, and that was rewarded. Your friend, Andre, or whatever his name is, did not—"

"That's not his fault! His parents—"

"It's also not my problem."

"Dad!"

"Mila."

"What about Uncle Yeva? You never would've gotten in without him."

"Yeva came here legally as well."

"My point is—"

"I know your point, *mayo solnyshka*. I'm just not in a place where I have the time nor inclination to rescue your rebound du jour, especially after I did so much for your last boyfriend only to find he's moving away."

There's so much to unpack here. Least of all is the fact that "rebound du jour" is the most laughable concept—I've literally never had a real boyfriend, rebound or otherwise, aside from Michael. But the comment that gets my attention, the one I couldn't ignore... "Michael's moving?"

"Guess he didn't mention that when he was breaking your heart."

"Tell me everything you know, Dad."

My dad sighs, and I can tell he's lost his patience. "Something about working at a horse show in the middle of nowhere, USAT?"

"He's going to work for USEF? In Kentucky?"

"That's the one. All those strings I pulled to get him that job and he repays me by leaving me in the lurch?" He has a few choice Ukrainian words for Michael, but I don't have time for it.

"Dad, I gotta go."

"Wait, but one more thing: did you get your applications in?"

"Not quite yet—"

"Mila, I don't know what I have to do to convince you this is crucial for your future."

"Dad—"

"Listen, if you don't get these in soon, I'm cutting off the horse funds."

"*Tato!*"

"Look, it's not a problem if you just get them in."

"Okay, okay. Gotta go, love you, bye."

I hang up and without even thinking, I dial Michael. The ringing reverberates through the speakers of my car. The sound travels all the way to my core, until I'm quivering with the need for him to *pick up the phone.* But of course it goes to voicemail. "Michael, call me back, please."

I press the hang-up button on my steering wheel to end the call and tighten my grip. I want to scream, to punch the wheel, to kick at the floor.

Michael is moving away? Am I really that bad, that he had to break up with me, rearrange his whole life, and now he's leaving the state?

A crushing sensation in my chest makes it hard to breathe, and I know I'm on the verge of a panic attack. I try to redirect my thoughts, reliving the show today, and practice my breathing—in for four seconds, hold for seven, out for eight. I repeat that several times until I'm sure I'm not about to lose it at 80 mph on I-75.

At home, my mom is asleep, face planted onto the kitchen table—a position I find her in frequently. Anya's monitor is propped in front of her, next to a mug of tea that's now cold, and a dog-eared novel. My mom works herself to the bone taking care of Anya, and often the only time she has to herself is after Anya falls asleep. Unfortunately, my mom is usually too tired to enjoy any of that alone time, and so I often find her here, knocked out. I take her tea to the sink, grab some water for myself, and then gently nudge her awake. She mutters something to me in a strange combination of Ukrainian and English that I don't quite catch, and then she stumbles up the stairs. I poke through the pantry, searching for something appealing, and end up grabbing a handful of chocolate chips from an opened bag in my mom's baking bin. I'm pretty sure it hasn't been used since before Anya's accident, and as I'm shoving another handful of chips into my mouth, I wonder if chocolate chips can go bad. I half-heartedly look for an expiration date, but I don't care enough, so I take another handful and go upstairs.

I wait outside of Anya's door for longer than usual, debating if I should go in and tell her about Michael. I want to, so desperately it hurts, but I also know it's selfish. She has enough to deal with, why should I add to that? But it's painful walking away from her door and closing myself, alone, in my room.

The rest of the show weekend passes in a strange blur. The show-grounds are oddly quiet—despite there being the same amount of horses on the grounds as before, there are significantly fewer people flocking around after the ICE raid. Riders are tacking up their own horses, leading them to the ring, getting on without leg-ups from grooms. I even see Beezie Madden leading a horse down the paths from the barns.

On Saturday, I have a rail in the first round so I don't get to go to the jump off, but on Sunday Cyrus and I have a spectacular ride and place second in the classic, which means we win money.

When we trailer the horses back to Trina's barn, I run into Alex. I was hoping we'd be able to pick up where we left off before the kiss, but things are perfectly awkward between us, with both of us going out of our way to be extra polite and not make eye contact all afternoon as we unload the horses and bring them to their stalls.

I'm in the tack room, cleaning my saddle, bridle and boots before storing them, when Alex walks in. He leans against the wall, his lanky form enacting a casualness I don't feel, and very nonchalantly says, "You wanna go to dinner tonight?" As if the thought just randomly popped into his head for no good reason.

I pause in the middle of scrubbing the dirt off my boots, every word in my vocabulary falling out of my head as though I'd just suffered a TBI.

After several moments without a response, Alex says, "I'll take that as a no."

"It's not that," I say, finally finding my words as I put my boots down and start on my saddle, even though I've already cleaned it. I'm fiddling with my stirrups, adjusting them needlessly, because I do *not* want to look at Alex. "It's just that, I dunno, you don't have to ask me out just because we...kissed."

And then he has the audacity to say, "It *was* a good kiss."

I'm so surprised at his statement that I glance up at him, and his dark brown eyes are dancing so playfully I find myself questioning whether he's being serious or not. But I've never known Alex to be a joker. His mouth quirks into a half-smile that zings through me like lightning. My face flushes as I continue to stare at him, and I'm sure he's reading me like a novel.

All of this has me wondering about our kiss, and it's replaying in my mind at 4k Ultra HD. I'm remembering the way his mouth felt against mine, his body pressed into me, and just like that my heart is thudding helplessly in my chest. Did I *want* to kiss him? If you had asked me beforehand, I would've said a definite no, but now I'm not so sure. Did he like kissing me? Is that what all of this is about? Despite everything I'm feeling about Michael, and our Breakup, I find myself blushing with the idea that Alex enjoyed kissing me—so much so that he's asking me out. And, if I'm being honest with myself, I'd probably go out with him if I were completely available. Which I'm not.

The fact of the matter is that I wanted to go out with the whole barn tonight so I could see Michael. If I went out with Alex, I'd miss out on that. Which is not something I'm willing to do, but I'm not sure how to say it.

"Um," is all I can muster before thank-the-heavens Trina blusters in and starts telling us we're going to Kickback tonight. I sigh, relieved, but Alex is still looking at me like he's waiting for my response. "I'll see you at Kickback?" I say.

Alex nods, and I can't tell if he's disappointed or relieved. Was he asking me out because he really wanted to go out with me, or was it out of obligation? As I'm standing there, overthinking everything, Alex grabs a container of horse treats and goes to walk out.

Before he leaves, he turns around and fixes me with a gaze. "I'll save you a seat, Mila." And even after he walks out, I can still see the look in his eyes burned in my mind. Something about it—the depth, the darkness, the blaze—makes my knees just a little bit weak.

It's too far for me to go back and forth from Wellington to home and back for dinner, so I shower and change at Trina's, which is only a couple miles from the showgrounds. I keep a few sets of clothes in my car just for this reason, since we often go out to dinner after the show on Sundays. Hoping Michael would be there, I packed an outfit I knew he'd love: a silk tank top with criss-crossing straps all down the back and a pair of high-waisted Sevens. I know Michael's not crazy about the fact that we're so close in height—he never liked when I wore high heels—so I wear some of my lowest cute shoes, a pair of flat yellow espadrilles.

I draw a perfect cat eye with my liquid eyeliner on my left eye, and a not-so-perfect one on my right side. Smoky eyes pair with red lips and my tousled, just-out-of-the-shower waves and I'm certain Michael will want to take me back the moment he sees me. Or at least have deep, unrelenting regret.

"Whoa there, cowgirl," Trina says when I exit the bathroom, "Are we hitting the club or just going to Kickback?"

I roll my eyes. "Everyone's going to be there, right?"

Trina grabs her purse and keys. "Yeah, *everyone*."

At Kickback Tavern, I'm agitated the moment I realize Michael's not there yet. I better not have gotten all dressed up for nothing.

We order drinks, but after a few sips I'm already feeling dizzy, since the only thing I've eaten today is my smoothie and a quick granola bar after my late afternoon ride.

At the other end of the table, Kayla and Ryan are debating who won last year's annual paintball tournament at the Conyer's show in Georgia. I can't find it in me to tell them it was definitely Ryan's team (AKA, *my* team). When the waitress drops off a basketful of greasy mozzarella sticks, I'm shoving one in my mouth before the basket hits the table. I know I need to be better about eating on show days—it's not healthy—but I don't know how to convince my queasy stomach what's best for it.

Alex saunters into the restaurant and takes a seat across from me just as I'm shoveling mozzarella stick number two into my mouth. I'm certain I look like a chipmunk gorging herself after a long winter.

"That's hot," he says with a crooked smile. "I'm beginning to understand why you didn't want to go out with me. But really, Mila, I can overcome your table manners."

I snort as I push the next mozzarella stick into my already full mouth, showing him how much I care about his views on my table manners. He laughs as I roll my eyes as if the sticks are the most delicious food I've ever eaten.

Just then, Michael walks up to the table, and I realize my mouth is too full to even attempt to chew my food. I quickly grab a napkin and force the food out of my mouth.

*Very sexy, Mila.* I blush furiously, my whole body on fire.

Suddenly I'm reliving the whole spectrum of feelings from our breakup, from devastated to angry to confused. I'm damaged, and I'm sure that everyone at the table will be able to see it, but no one is looking at me, except maybe Alex. No one's noticing as I fall apart yet again.

Meanwhile, Michael is looking at everyone *but* me. His dirty blond hair is longer than it was the last time I saw him up close. It's falling in his blue eyes and he's running a hand through it like he just walked off the set of a '90s episode of *Baywatch*, except that he's wearing a shirt, which is unfortunate.

Alex follows my gaze, and his mouth tightens almost imperceptibly. There's a distant part of my brain that's telling me I should do something other than stare at Michael. Join in the conversation at the end of the table, flirt with Alex, clean my dirty nails, literally *anything* except what I'm doing right now. But instead, I stare. And Michael continues to avoid my gaze as he greets the rest of the barn crew, idling at the other end of the table.

I remember, then, my runaway text from last week and the phone call he didn't bother to return and realize that *that* was our last interaction. Not that you can call it an interaction, per se, because he didn't react. But the thought brings even more warmth to my cheeks and another wave of frozen indecision.

Everything stills as Michael's eyes finally meet mine. His gaze takes me back to the Breakup. We were at Kickback when it happened. Michael had been acting distant and weird all week—taking forever to return my texts, giving me lame reasons he couldn't hang out. At Kickback with the barn, he sat next to Ryan, across from me instead of beside me, and basically ignored me the whole time.

A year ago, I would've cornered him, demanding to know what in the world his deal is. But now, this walking-on-eggshells Mila took it on the chin. And it made me feel like crap. When I finished my burger, I dropped a twenty on the table and left.

No one seemed to notice.

I was all the way to my car when Michael came running out. And I felt relieved. The thought makes me cringe now, because I thought he cared.

I was so, so wrong.

"Hey, Milly," Michael said, and I didn't even care that he called me by my hated nickname because I was just happy he'd run after me. "Can we talk?"

I raised an eyebrow, trying to act like I was mad at him when I was just pathetically happy he ran after me. "What's up?"

"I just wanted to talk to you."

I crossed my arms over my chest. "It hasn't seemed like you've wanted to talk all week."

Michael rubbed the back of his neck awkwardly, and this was my first clue that something was wrong. It's his tell; when he doesn't know what to say or he's second guessing himself. "I know, it's just..."

I stepped closer to him, because even though he was in the process of breaking my heart, I still wanted to be near him. "Michael, what's wr—"

"This isn't working." He shot the words out like daggers, his face unyielding, almost hard. My brain went blank for a moment because I couldn't really wrap my head around what he was implying.

"This"—I waved a finger back and forth between us—"isn't working?"

"We're just different people now."

My brain finally snapped into go-mode and I snarked, "Did you just read a book on cliché breakup lines, Michael? Couldn't come up with any good reasons on your own?"

He stepped back, raising his hands palms up like he was innocent. The audacity. "I'm not trying to hurt you, Mila."

"Well, you failed."

"We're just going in different directions."

"Different directions? Are you serious, Michael? As of a week ago we were literally going in the exact same direction—we'd planned that direction together, if I recall correctly. Both of us interning with my dad over the summer, applying to the same grad schools. You—you even—" My hands went to my head because I couldn't even believe it. I couldn't get the words out. "You talked about, about, *marriage*, Michael. You brought it up, not me. I believe your exact words were, 'We'll get engaged sometime during grad school and get married when we graduate.' Those were your words less than a month ago. You—you winked at me when you said it."

I'm not sure why I felt like that last part was necessary, but the scene was so clear in my mind. I remembered every second, every breath, every look he gave me that night because I thought that this was the beginning of the rest of my life. And now it was all over. Because, why? It's still unclear to me.

"I know, I know, Mila." Michael at least has the awareness to look mortified, which didn't make me feel better at all, "I really messed up. I had so much regret after that conversation—"

"Stop. Just, stop." I put my hand out, cutting him off. A girl could only take so much. How could two people have the same conversation and walk away with such different emotions? I was so over-the-moon that day, and Michael...he felt regret? How is that possible?

"Mila—" He reached out for me and I backed away. I wish I'd had something clever, something snarky or even mean to say, but I had nothing.

The only move I had was to leave.

So I did.

That was a couple weeks ago, and now I'm sitting back in Kickback, staring at Michael like the loser that I am. Alex is saying something to me so I rip my gaze from Michael's and return to Alex.

"Hm?"

"Did you want to order?" Alex points a thumb at the waitress, who I definitely did not notice standing beside me.

"Oh, right, yes." I look dumbly through the menu, though I'm not really seeing anything, and I've been here so many times I don't need to look at the menu at all.

"Want to split some wings?" Alex offers when it becomes clear I'm not choosing anything. I agree, and the waitress asks if I want a refill on my lager, but I shake my head.

By the time she moves on to the rest of the table, Michael is gone. I stand up and look around. I think I see him in the back near the bar, so I head that way, but it's not him. I make my way across the dance floor, looking desperately for him while praying I don't *look* desperate.

When I don't find him inside, I step into the parking lot, only to find his Tacoma squealing out of the parking lot. A violent emptiness rips through me and I turn on my heel and stumble back into the restaurant.

# Chapter Five

# Past Tense

I walk back to the table, and even though my world is being ripped apart, it seems as though nothing has changed for anyone else. I sit down across from Alex, who's fixing me with a gaze I can't quite interpret. He has a book open in front of him, which seems odd in the middle of dinner with a bunch of people, but I don't question him. Amber's clearly trying to talk with him, making remarks about the ICE raid, but he's clearly trying to read his book.

"You, uh, okay?" he asks. As soon as Amber senses the conversation is not going to revolve around her, she turns away to chat up Katie. There's something about the fact that he obviously didn't want to talk with Amber but he *does* want to talk with me that makes the tiniest bit of warmth trickle through my veins.

I consider lying and telling him I'm alright, that I just needed to go to the bathroom. But something about the look in his eyes makes me feel like I can be real with him. "Not really."

I expect him to ask me questions, or to offer solutions, or even to bash Michael, but he doesn't. "I'm sorry," he says, and I believe him.

"I'm not sure I'll ever be okay," I confess quietly.

"It would be shocking if you were," he says. "You've been through a lot this year. No one who's gone through what you've gone through would be anywhere close to okay."

I glance up at him as I realize that he's right. This past year could be an eighth circle in Dante's *Inferno*: watching your loved one get paralyzed and being completely helpless to do anything about it. And if what he's saying is true—which, it is—why has no one else acknowledged it?

I realize, sitting there at a table full of my friends, that no one has expressed to me the simple statement that Alex just said: it's been hard. For *me*. Not just for Anya, not just for my parents, but for me.

I'm not trying to be selfish or take away from what Anya is going through, but it's as if people think that either a.) I'm fine even though my sister's not or b.) it's safer to just not talk about it, because it'll bring up messy emotions. And who wants that? Certainly not me.

And yet, I didn't realize how much I *needed* someone to say the simple truth of what Alex just said. It's been rough.

But between my mom wanting me to be sister of the year with Anya, my dad pressuring me to pick up the slack where Anya left off with being daughter of the year, and Trina wanting me to be competitor of the year—how is there anything left in me to just...be?

"I can tell there's a lot going on up there," Alex says, closing his book. "Do you want to talk about it?"

Another thing no one's asked me. Do my friends just suck, am I *that* closed off, or does no one in the universe know how to deal with life-altering tragedies? This is why I stick to the horses, because they don't let you down in the same way that people do.

"I know I need to talk about it at some point but..." I twiddle with the silverware, flipping them around on the napkin. "I'm just not ready."

Alex nods. "I get that."

"How so?" I ask, curious as to how he knows to say the right thing. "That is, um, if you don't mind me asking. You don't have to tell me anything you don't want to."

One side of his mouth lifts in a sad smile and he says, "My dad died, five years ago."

"Oh wow, I-I had no idea. I'm so sorry."

"Thanks."

I'm feeling a little guilty that I've worked alongside Alex at the barn for so many years without even knowing about his dad. Alex has always been pretty private, and I've never thought to ask more about his life. I'm wondering, then, if that's how people feel about me.

A quietness stretches between us, and it's clear that even though Alex knows the right thing to say in a tragedy, I do not. So I do what any respectable human would do: I change the subject.

"Hey, any news on Bastien?" I ask, referring to one of the grooms that was picked up in the ICE raid.

Alex shakes his head. "Trina's trying to call around and see what she can do. To be honest, I'm not sure there is anything she can do. Especially since Bastien has a record."

"Wow, that sucks. It's crazy how your life can change just like that. One minute you're working your job, the next minute you're being deported."

"Well, it takes a while to actually get deported, but I get what you're saying."

I kind of want to make up for not asking more about Alex's life before, so I probe a little. "How are you feeling, y'know, after everything? Are you worried or anything? That's not, like, a normal thing, is it? For Immigration to just show up at the showgrounds? I've never noticed that before." Okay, maybe I went a little overboard with all of the questions, but now I genuinely want to know.

"It hasn't happened since I've been around, but Carlos told me that ICE raided about ten years ago, same thing. They're just doing their job." He shrugs, but his eyes betray more feeling than the casual gesture did. "I guess there's always going to be a part of me that's worried about something like that. I mean, I am here illegally." He cringes at the word. "But, I keep my hands clean, stay under the radar, and I'm in college, so as long as I have someone to rescue me in freak raids like that"—he gives a quirk of his mouth that makes my stomach flip—"I think I'll be okay."

I take a sip of water, my mouth dry at the memory of the kiss. "What about getting a lawyer?"

Alex nods. "We will, one day. Right now pretty much every cent I make goes toward food and my mom's healthcare. It's not cheap." He looks away, like he's embarrassed by this fact, and I want to tell him he doesn't have to be, but I don't. I have a feeling it would only make him feel worse.

"Is your mom at risk for being deported, too?"

He sighs and starts fidgeting with his beer bottle, turning it in circles on the coaster. I've made him uncomfortable, and I feel bad. I suppose this is how people feel when they ask me about Anya. "My mom's not a citizen or legal resident, if that's what you're asking. I don't think she'll get deported, though. She barely leaves the house, and unless I get...taken, and say something, I don't think there's anyone else besides maybe Trina that really knows her situation."

Before I can say anything else, the waitress arrives with our wings and my stomach gives a loud gurgle. The food arriving seems to shift the conversations around the table, and suddenly Amber is thigh-to-thigh with me, checking out our wings and asking me about my ride. We chat a bit, and I notice that as soon as Amber comes over, Alex goes back to reading his book: *Black Hole Survival Guide*. I can't decide if I think it's cool that he's reading in the middle of dinner, or rude. He definitely seems on the verge of being rude to Amber, which is fine by me, but I do wonder about it.

Amber eats several of our wings, the whole time complaining about the shrimp she chose. I want to somehow find a way to ask her about Michael without being too obvious. Instead, I just order her another drink and lo and behold, twenty minutes later she leans in and says, "Mikey's really trying to avoid you, huh?"

*Mikey*? I try to act casual and not at all like the bitter ex-girlfriend that's raging inside of me. "Yeah, what do you think is up with that?" I have to half-shout into her ear because the band has started up and they're playing Katy Perry's "California Girls" just a decibel too loud for conversation.

"Girl, I thought you'd tell me. He literally has been asking me to tell him whenever you get to the barn or leave or when you're in the middle of riding so he can come and do his thing with Khan. Like what in the world, are we back in middle school or what?" She snorts into her beer, and then realizes it's empty so she's waving down the waitress for another round.

I sit back. So Amber's been the mole in the barn telling Michael about my whereabouts. I feel a pain in my stomach as if I've been punched in the gut. Alex glances at me over his book.

As if he knows I want to get away from Amber posthaste, he says, "Want to dance?"

How does this guy know how to make me speechless again and again? "Um," I say eloquently.

He holds out his hand, and after a beat too long, I take it and let him pull me up from the table.

Am I really going to dance with him? He's still holding my hand, and I realize I haven't held a guy's hand, except for Michael's, in *years*. His are calloused and strong, yet he's holding mine gently and I don't want to let go, except I can't do this. I tug on his hand, and he turns to face me. He's so close, and his hands are hovering like they want to go around my waist, but they don't.

"Alex?"

"Yeah?" His dark eyes are drawing me in like a pair of black holes, and I have this disjointed thought that maybe that's why he's reading about black holes. Maybe *I* need a survival guide. I have to take a step back from him, or else I'm going past the point of no return.

"I can't, I'm sorry, I'm not..." Available? Capable of having another relationship?

"It's okay, Mila," he says, and then he's running his hands down my arms and I swear it feels like he's running a hand down my back because of the tingle that's going up and down my spine. What in the world is going on?

"I gotta go," I say. "Can I Venmo you for the wings?"

He shakes his head. "Don't worry about it. I wanted to take you out anyway, remember?" He looks around for a second and then returns his gaze to me. "I had a different place in mind, but, maybe next time?"

I nod noncommittally. "Right. Next time." The whole thing makes me squirm. I take out my phone, trying to exert some control over the situation. "What's your name on Venmo?"

I'm unlocking my phone, but Alex puts his hand on top of it. "Mila, I'm serious, it's fine."

"I'll just—"

"How about this? Instead of paying me a few dollars for the wings, just promise me something."

"Okay?"

"The next time I ask you to dance, say yes." He squeezes my hand and walks away before I can give a rebuttal.

As I drive away from Kickback Tavern, my phone automatically connects via Bluetooth to my car and plays my Breakup playlist. "If the World was Ending" by JP Saxe and Julia Michaels plays first and I just want to *be* the notes in this song. The music gets inside my veins, and I'm belting about how it's over and it's fine, but it's not fine and I think my heart is turning to ash. Michael left my heart and soul to burn, and the tiniest puff of air will blow away whatever's left.

It's why I can't even begin to entertain Alex's attention—how fair would that be to him, anyway? He deserves all that a girl can give him, and I'm not that girl. Not today, maybe not ever.

But I can't deny how much I was craving for someone to *see* me and the hardships I've been going through. I didn't even realize how much I needed it until Alex did that for me. It's strange how something so simple can be so meaningful.

Why hadn't Michael done that for me? Or had he done it, and I'd just forgotten? The days and weeks after Anya's accident are such a blur, it's hard to remember what people said or did then. Perhaps my friends *did* say and do the right thing, but I was just too shell-shocked to know. That's the thing about tragedies like this—everyone else eventually moves on, but you have to live with it.

At home, I stand at Anya's door with my palm stretched out on the door, as if I can feel her through the composite wood. It's completely silent and I know she's asleep, so I crack the door. My mom is knocked out on the cot beside Anya's bed, so I walk in.

The only light in the room is from the moonlight filtering through the window. Anya's asleep on her back, a pillow under her knees and her hair fanned out around her head. She's thinner than usual, her cheekbones sharp and angular, her dark lashes contrasting against her pale skin. She's lovely, even like this. My mom clearly brushed Anya's hair against the pillow, and something about the way her hair is arranged around her face makes her look like she's dead. The thought hits me like a blow to the chest and I rush from the room, close the door, and collapse outside in the hallway. I'm clutching at my chest, gasping for air, trying to erase the image from my mind.

*Anya's alive.* She's alive, I tell myself.

I stumble to my shower and sit in the stream, the water pouring over me until it runs cold, trying not to picture my sister's body in a casket.

When Tuesday rolls around, I call Trina on my way to the barn.

"Hey, is Michael there?" I ask.

"You mean Alex?"

I can't help it, I choke on my coffee.

"I've got eyeballs, chica, and at least half a brain still functioning up there, despite Blue's best efforts."

"I'm calling about *Michael*, Trina."

"I know, and I'm telling you about Alex."

"Fine, humor me, is Alex at the barn?"

"Well, seeing as he lives here, yeah, he's here."

"He lives...wait, he lives at the barn?"

"Uh, yeah, only for about five years now."

Five years. Alex mentioned on Sunday that his dad had passed five years ago, which means they moved here when his dad died. "Gosh, he's lived at the barn this whole time and I've had no idea," I say more to myself than Trina.

"Yes, Detective Mila, a good number of the grooms live here, actually."

"But what about his mom? He has a mom."

"I gotta tell you something," Trina says with a laugh. "Everyone has a mom, my friend."

I roll my eyes at my own dumb comment, even though she can't see me. "Yeah, I figured that one out. I meant, does his mom live there, too?"

"She does."

"Huh. How come I've never met her?"

"What is this, twenty questions? Are you coming to the barn or not? Just wanna know 'cause I'm happy to charge Daddy Big Bucks for flatting your horse for you."

"No, no, I'm coming. And oh my gosh, Trina, don't ever call him that to his face."

"Too cringy?"

"No, he'd love it way too much. I couldn't live with him and his big head."

Trina laughs. "Alright, I'll let Alex know you're coming."

"No!" I say a little too hastily. "Actually, can you tell whoever is around that I'm not coming?"

"But you just said..."

"I know, I know, but if Amber is there, or within earshot, can you just say I'm not coming today?"

"Riiiight, okay. I'm not asking questions this time because I've got a lesson waiting for me, but you won't get away so easy next time."

"Thanks, Trina."

"You bet."

When I pull up to the barn, sure enough, Michael's black Tacoma is there. I check my reflection in the mirror, swiping on some lip gloss and a coat of mascara. I take down my hair so that my light brown waves fall around my shoulders. I try to give myself a little pep talk about how I'm worthy of love, anyone would be lucky to have me, but I must not be very good at pep talks because I still feel jittery as I walk into the barn. I don't see Michael in the aisleway, so I make my way to the tack room.

He's standing there, adjusting Khan's bridle on the far wall, and I want to say something but my heart is stuck in my throat. He turns as I walk in, and as soon as he sees me, his face falls.

"Mila," he says in a tight voice.

"Michael." I take a deep breath, trying to force oxygen into my lungs, even as they're seemingly rejecting it. "Can we talk?"

He turns back to the bridle, and I can't tell if he's actually fixing something or if he's just fiddling with it so he doesn't have to look at me. "What do you want to talk about?"

I notice he doesn't bring up my cringy text, or that he got my voicemail. Is this how things are going to be with us? After *two years* he's just going to act like my texts or calls aren't worth returning?

"I don't even really know why you ended things. I need closure, Michael."

"Closure?" He glances back at me and his eyes are wide and drowning with sadness. I'm so confused because *he* broke up with *me*, what does he have to be sad about? "That's all?"

"Yes," I say, though it's nowhere close to all I want.

He steps away from the bridle and plops down on his tack trunk, his elbows on his knees. He's got his boot socks *over* his breeches, which I never understood—they're supposed to go *under* so you don't get scratched by the Velcro. They're mismatched socks too, which used to seem lazy and now it just seems...endearing. He's looking down at his hands, his hair falling in his eyes. My hands twitch with the desire to run my fingers through his hair, but I don't move.

"It's just, I don't know," he begins, "after Anya's thing, you're so...different."

"Anya's *thing*? My sister is crippled, forever, Michael. As in, for the rest of her life."

"I know, I know. What am I supposed to say? I've said it a thousand times, I'm sorry." Has he, though? "It's just..." he trails off, and he's looking at me, really taking me in for the first time since I got into the tack room. A flush goes through me, and I'm hoping, praying, he likes what he sees.

He looks away.

"It's been hard for me, too," he says.

"I'm sorry, how has it been hard for you?" I can't help it, my voice rises and it gets a little squeaky, a fact that my dad has drilled me on constantly. *Men won't respect you if you sound like a mouse.* I clear my throat.

"I mean with the panic attacks and everything—"

"You mean, *my* panic attacks?"

"Yeah, it's, y'know, hard when I loved you and I wanted you to be happy..."

It hits me like I've just gotten bucked off. The shock of one second being on your horse, and the next second you're flying through the air, hitting the ground with a painful *thud.*

*Loved.* As in, past tense.

Michael continues talking, about how he tried to fix me, but couldn't, and I just can't take it.

"Here's the thing," I interrupt him, my voice raising another octave, and I know my dad would be ashamed but I don't care. "Sometimes, the people you love are not happy, and they can't make themselves be happy, and honestly you're going to have a hard time loving *anybody* if you can't deal with the good times *and* the bad."

"I know that, Mila, and I tried. It's not like Anya's accident happened yesterday. It was a year ago. I get that you're mourning, I get that you're sad, but it just feels like you *want* to be that way, like you're punishing yourself or something. And you refuse to get help."

I cross my arms over my chest. "Just tell me if your idea of a fun time is pouring your soul out to a perfect stranger that's charging you by the hour."

"You only gave that lady one try."

"It was a disaster!"

"Look, it's not even about the therapy thing. It's just a whole lot of things together. For cryin' out loud, you have Cyrus Van der Bergh—a horse that would jump over the moon for you—and you're going in the Low Amateur's? That's not the Mila I know."

"Do I need to remind you what happened to my sister *on* Cyrus while they were 'jumping over the moon?'" I say with air quotes.

"It doesn't change the fact that the old Mila would've moved up the second she got the chance. Don't you remember when Anya got Cyrus? You were so jealous you couldn't talk about anything else for a week. And now he's yours and you're wasting it."

The silence stretches and hardens between us like ice.

"It's not that simple, Michael, and you know it," I say through gritted teeth.

He sighs, his whole body slumping. "I know, it's just that we're so young."

"What does that have to do with anything?"

"This is the time in our lives when we're supposed to be having fun, getting out, taking risks, having adventures, not, y'know, sitting on the couch watching sad movies every night."

It feels like someone's holding a match to my veins. My blood is boiling, and I'm about to lose it all over Michael. "I gotta tell you, it's really enlightening to hear you synthesize our relationship like that. Thanks for the clarity."

"I'm not making this up—"

"No one said you were. But think of it from my point of view—I'm still getting my feet under me with Anya's *thing,* and then you rip the rug out from beneath me. You said you were in love with me, you told me you wanted to spend the rest of your life with me."

I'm standing in the middle of the tack room, feeling so nakedly vulnerable, wishing I could make myself cry so as to elicit some sort of feeling in Michael. I want him to feel regret for breaking my heart, for hurting me so deeply at literally the worst time in my life. And, if I'm being honest, I want him to take it all back, and I know that if he said right this second that he'd made a mistake, we'd get back together. I would forgive him and never remind him *once* of what he'd done.

I wait for him to stand up, to hold me in his arms, to say he's sorry.

I wait, but it never happens.

I feel like he's gutted me and he's just standing there, watching me bleed out in front of him.

I turn away, grabbing my saddle off the rack, because I'm not sure I want him to see how broken I am.

I grip the pommel of my saddle, overwhelmed by the insanity of this situation. Michael and I were supposed to be together. We'd had our whole life planned together after college. Why was he screwing it all up? Because I hadn't felt like partying with him lately?

With my back turned to him, Michael mumbles something about needing to go, and slips out of the tack room. Just like that.

For a moment, my fury burns against Anya. This is her fault. If she hadn't crashed through that jump, she'd still be here, I'd still have my whole life ahead of me with Michael, and I wouldn't have all the pressure from Dad and everyone else in my life.

But as quickly as the thought blazes in my mind, it dies away. I can't blame Anya—not really. Fate, maybe. But Anya didn't ask for any of this—far from it.

I take a deep breath, grit my teeth, and walk out of the tack room, keeping my head as high as I can possibly hold it. Which is to say, I'm looking straight at the ground.

As I turn the corner, I run, quite literally, into Alex.

"Oops," he says, catching me and my saddle. "I got you."

"Sorry," I mumble. "Head's not screwed on right today."

He laughs. "When is it ever?"

"Hey!" I snap out of my funk long enough to smack him on the arm.

"Tacking up Cyrus?" He's still holding my saddle, and starts walking down the breezeway with me toward Cyrus's stall.

"Yeah, just doing a light flat today. I'll probably take him for a trail ride."

"I was just about to tack up Kobe, can I join you?"

"Oh, sure," I say, because what else can I say? *No, I want to brood on horseback by myself?*

We groom and saddle up our horses, and he gives me a leg up. I watch as he swings his long legs onto Kobe, a chestnut Dutch Warmblood who's owned by a doctor who comes for lessons once a week. The rest of the time, either Trina or someone else at the barn rides him to keep him in shape. I've ridden him a few times and he's a steady mover and a very scopey jumper.

We hack the horses on the grass field outside of the sand arena, passing each other in comfortable silence. I've never really paid attention to Alex riding before—he's usually grooming, not riding—but he's unsurprisingly a very capable rider, although his posture is a little lacking and his stirrups seem a tad long. But Kobe is moving nicer than I've ever seen him move, so there's probably a method to his madness.

While we ride, I'm replaying the conversation with Michael in my mind. And then I'm drifting back to my birthday this past November when Michael rented a boat for us. He strung it with twinkle lights and ordered out from my favorite restaurant. There was a table on the boat, which he'd topped with a table cloth, flowers and little tea lights. Of course none of that stayed put the moment he started driving the boat, which made us laugh hysterically when it all ended up in a pile on the floor of the boat, the table cloth singed by the candles. We had dinner under the stars in what felt like the middle of the ocean—it truly seemed like we were the only people in all of the world that night. We ate and danced and talked and looked at the stars. I'll never forget when we were looking up at the sky, marveling at how many more stars we could see only a couple miles from the city lights, and he said to me, "All those stars are looking at you, marveling at your beauty, wishing they were you." I'd kissed him then, with every ounce of love in my body.

What's ironic about the whole thing is I'd thought there was a chance he was going to propose. I know that we're so young, but the whole thing was so romantic, and he was so expressive that night, I was certain the only reason he'd done all that was to put a ring on my finger. I would've said yes. Real talk: I'd still say yes right now. And that's the thought that has me feeling utterly alone even as Alex and I circle each other on horseback.

After we've worked the horses, we walk them down the gravel drive out onto the trails. Cyrus is relaxed, his giant gray ears flopping on either side of his head, not pointing in any particular direction. Kobe is more alert, eyes and ears paying special attention to every bush we pass. It's the afternoon, and even though it's winter, it's still Florida, so that means it's hot. The sun blazes down on us, and my skin is warm with it. Our horses are only lightly sweating from the workout, but the back of my shirt is moist, as is Alex's. Once we get out on the trails, though, there's a nice breeze and we all start to cool off.

"I, uh, overheard some of your conversation with Michael," Alex says quietly. "I wasn't trying to eavesdrop or anything. It's just, well, it got a little loud."

I groan. "Fantastic."

We walk in silence, the horses' hooves clopping in tandem on the trail. After a while I say, "Isn't this the part where you're supposed to bash Michael?"

Alex laughs. "Seemed like you were doing a fine job of it yourself." He smiles at me. "Besides, if I did that, would that make me the hero or the villain?"

"Hmm." Cyrus flicks one ear back at us, as if he's listening. "That's, kind of...profound."

"That's my diabolical plan, to show you how profound I am." He winks at me, and I can't help but crack a smile. "I just wanted to be honest with you about what I heard."

"I appreciate that."

"We can talk about it if you want," he says.

"Or?"

"Or...we could forget about Michael for the next half hour and just have a really nice trail ride."

"I like that option."

"Me too." And then Alex gives me a full-fledged smile and I do, in fact, forget about Michael for a moment.

# Chapter Six

# Radical Acceptance

I learn quite a bit about Alex on our trail ride, including why he likes to read in a crowd.

"After my dad died, it's like a part of me faded away. I shut down. I was constantly bending over backward to make other people happy, because I couldn't even think about my own happiness, and I didn't know what I needed."

"I get that."

He glances over at me. "I know you do," he says in that quiet way of his as his eyes linger on mine, bringing warmth to my cheeks.

"So," I say, breaking away from his gaze, "what helped?"

"Honestly? Time. Although grief does fundamentally change you—I'm not ever going back to what I was like before my dad died."

"Hmm." What he was saying hit a little too close to home. A part of me wanted him to stop, to bury this topic and never come back, but a bigger part of me was desperate to hear of another person actually dealing with their grief in a seemingly productive way.

"My mom practically forced me into therapy," he says with a grimace. "I think she was worried she would lose my dad *and* me."

"What was that like for you, going to therapy?"

"It saved my life," he says matter-of-factly. "I figured out what I needed in order to cope."

We're walking past a row of Ficus hedges, and Kobe turns his nose toward them and snorts at something on the other side of the hedge.

Alex rubs a hand down Kobe's neck and shushes him, calming the horse almost instantly.

"What did you need?" I ask once we're past the hedges.

"Well, that's a loaded question, but one thing I figured out is that as an introvert, I'm overwhelmed by being around a lot of people, but as someone who was dealing with a lot of grief, I needed to not be alone. So that's where the compromise came in—I would go out with friends, but I'd bring a book for when I needed it."

"Hmm." My mind drifts back to dinner on Sunday, sitting across from Alex while he read his book. "Maybe you should, I dunno, tell people about it, so they don't think you're being...rude?"

Alex slants his eyes at me and says, "Did you think I didn't want to talk with you on Sunday?"

"Well, I–I..." I lift my hands up in a shrug. I'll be honest, I knew that he wanted to talk to me—it was obvious, with the way he ignored Amber and not me. But I want to hear it.

"Mila, in what universe would I not want to talk to you?"

"I don't know, this one?"

He tosses his head back and laughs. I haven't seen this side of Alex before. He's always so serious, so diligent in his work at the barn, I'm not sure I've ever seen him really laugh before. Not like this. The sound is musical and deep, and I find myself admiring him—the firm shape of his jaw, the little bit of afternoon stubble glinting off his cheek, his straight-line nose and dark, inquiring brows. Once he's done laughing, I wait for him to say more, but he doesn't.

I'm wondering a little at myself. Why do I want acknowledgement from him that he wants to talk to me? To be around me? Am I just trying to stroke my own ego after it took a big blow with Michael? Or is it something more?

We turn right at the next trail, a sand path that will lead us back to Zen Elite.

"Are you studying...astronomy?" I ask, guessing based on his book of choice from the other night, though I'm only really asking to change the subject in my mind. I do not want to analyze my feelings about Alex just yet.

"Oh, no, I'm not. Just interested in it. I'm studying business, hoping to one day open my own place."

"What kind of place?"

"I have some ideas, but haven't settled on 'the one.' Not yet."

The conversation shifts to me and my plans after I graduate from UM. I tell him about the business schools my dad has selected for me to apply to.

"So that's what the talented Mila Kozak wants to do with her life, huh? MBA? Are you going to join your dad's business after?"

"I think that's his plan."

"And you? What do you want?"

"Who knows?"

"Well, you should." The horses' plodding hooves mark the silence that lingers between us when I don't give him an answer. "Isn't there anything that you think of, I don't know, right before you fall asleep at night? Or an idea that keeps you awake at night because it's so thrilling? What do you dream about?"

"I'm not the dreaming type. More like the nightmaring type." I shrug. "Besides, it's not really like that for me. Not with my family, especially not after Anya."

"I understand that, albeit in a different way. With my dad gone and my mom's health not great, I can't just go off and do whatever I want. That's why I'm working here, so we have a place to live and I can still take classes at night."

"I didn't know all of that. What happened with your mom?"

"She has epilepsy. That's why we came here in the first place, to get proper treatment. They didn't have anything for her back in Cuba, and my dad, well, he would do anything for my mom."

As he spoke about his parents—their love for each other, the way they all braved the open ocean in a tiny boat to come here in order to help his mom—it makes me sad for my parents. Why couldn't they have that, too? Or maybe they did have it and just lost it.

"...when my dad died, my mom's epilepsy got a lot worse. Stress always makes her have more episodes, and most of the time she can't keep a job."

"I'm sorry, Alex." I'm only just starting to realize the gravity of what almost happened with the ICE raid at the showgrounds—if Alex had been arrested, what would that mean for his mom? An involuntary shudder runs through me at the thought. "That's...a lot."

"It is what it is." And the way he says it, there's no bitterness in his voice, not even resignation. He actually sounds like he's at peace with it, which is so far from how I feel about, well, just about everything.

"Did you learn that in therapy?" I joke.

"Actually, I did. It's called radical acceptance."

"Okay, you just made that up."

"Google it."

"I will, but if it's something weird, you owe me."

"I'd love to owe you one. In fact, let's just say I owe you dinner."

"Wow." I shake my head and laugh. "You are persistent."

Alex is quiet for a moment, and I think he's not going to respond but then he says, "Here's the thing, Mila. I've thought about what I want. And maybe if you thought about what you want, you'd go out to dinner with me." His words are so assertive, and yet his delivery is so gentle, I almost miss what he's saying.

"I–I'll think about it."

He smiles and steals a glance at me, his dark eyes washing over me. "I'd like that."

It's that look that I'm thinking about the whole drive home. Even as I drift back to my conversation with Michael and I agonize over how to win him back, my mind flits to Alex's gaze on mine over and over again.

At home, my mom is getting ready for our monthly family dinner. The first few times we had our family dinner, my dad actually carried Anya down the stairs and we all sat around the dining table. It was disastrous. Every time he attempted to bring her down, my mom would lose her marbles and they would fight horribly. He never did it right and he would eventually shout at her to do it herself, and then they were fighting over Anya like she was a doll instead of an actual human being. I hated it. I'm pretty sure my parents wouldn't be separated if we didn't have family dinners. Or if Anya hadn't had her accident.

After a couple months of the same old issues, we came up with a compromise—we brought a folding table and chairs up to the second floor landing and we would eat there. Anya could sit in her wheelchair and we would eat our take-out on the makeshift dining table.

Today, we're eating Suri Sushi Thai and my mom is cutting up Anya's sushi to feed to her. Before Anya's accident, we used to do 'highs and lows' during our dinner—we would each share the best part of our day and the worst part. But now, there's not really any point to it. We all have the same low, and sometimes there's just not a high that's high enough to share.

Anya's in her wheelchair, looking like a very sad doll with her pale, porcelain skin and her somber blue eyes. It's quiet around the table as we eat. My dad used to badger Anya about continuing her education at Stanford online, but that ended months ago. Now, he's just focusing all his attention on me.

"You get your oil changed?" he asks me between bites.

"I get it changed every three months. I have a reminder on my phone." *Like you made me do nine months ago*, I don't bother adding.

"Your car's going to stop running if you don't take care of it. Have them wash it and vacuum it out when you go next time. Not that you horse people care about the stink."

I take a tiny bit of wasabi and mix it with soy sauce and dip my sushi in it a little too aggressively so that it splashes onto the plastic table. "It doesn't stink."

He gives me a face like I've clearly just lost all my olfactory senses.

"What classes do you have this semester?"

I tell my dad what I'm registered for and he finds a way to lecture me about getting my schoolwork done even though my classes don't start till tomorrow.

"You guys watching any good shows these days?" I ask my mom and Anya, because it's the only light topic I can think of to discuss with them. My mom is overjoyed to have some conversation directed toward Anya. If she were a dog, she'd be wagging her tail obnoxiously right about now.

"We're watching The 100," my mom says. "Tell them about it, Anya."

"Nuclear warfare forces a portion of humankind into space and after a hundred years," she says as if quoting directly from Netflix, "they send a bunch of teen delinquents back to the ground to see if it's safe." Her voice is husky from disuse, and just hearing her voice sparks a desire in me to just *hear* her. To sit and talk with her for hours like we used to.

Except nothing is as it used to be.

"Interesting," I say, because what else can I say?

"It's completely unrealistic, these teens always saving the world," my dad remarks gruffly.

I roll my eyes, and go to give Anya a look, but she doesn't meet my eye.

And that pretty much sums up our family dinners.

# Chapter Seven

# Horse People Problems

Wednesday is my first day back in classes for the Spring semester. In my Law of Financial Transactions class, the professor greets me like an old friend. He's a short, thin man with a thick beard and wearing a Nike polo shirt that seems to be almost shiny, like it's waterproof. He's my dad's age, give or take a few years.

"Mila! Good to see you, dear."

I'm looking down at my schedule to check his name and I'm scrambling—have I taken a class with him and forgotten? Ludlow. Professor Ludlow. Not familiar at all.

"Your father told me you'd be in my class this semester." Ah, so that explains it.

"I'm looking forward to it," I lie.

"He mentioned that you might need a letter of recommendation for your graduate school applications."

"I haven't taken your class yet—"

"Oh." He laughs as if that's a minor impediment. "After so many years, I'm able to deduce a student's character very quickly."

"Right," I say, wondering if somehow my dad paid this guy off, or if my Law of Financial Transactions professor thinks he's above it all. "Well, I appreciate that, Professor."

"Come by during my office hours anytime."

"Thanks," I mumble as I take a seat in the back.

After class, I sneak out behind some other students so I don't have to interact with Professor Ludlow any more than strictly necessary. I'm tempted to call my dad and ask him what he did to Ludlow to make him so chummy with me, but I don't want to confess to him that I haven't finished my essay yet. I think back to our conversation last week, when he threatened to withdraw my horse funding. Would he do that? And what would that even mean? Could he stop paying for Cyrus's food and board?

I have two more classes today—Stochastic Models in Operations Research and an Afro-Caribbean Art History class. After, I meet up with Monica at the Starbucks in the student center. She squeals and hugs me as if we haven't seen each other for ages. I guess it has been six weeks, but it still feels a bit over-the-top. But that's one of the things I've always loved about Monica: she wears her heart tattooed on her forehead.

She's dressed to the nines—she always is—in high heels, a pencil skirt, and flowing white blouse. Her dark hair is swept up in a perfect, I-did-this-by-accident messy bun, with just the right amount of stray hairs framing her face. I feel scrubby in comparison in my jeans and tank top, but I got used to feeling this with Monica years ago.

We order our drinks and sit down to catch up. She obviously knows about my Breakup—not because I told her, but because Michael took down all of our pictures together on Instagram one night and it set her off. I tell her about my runaway text, which causes her to go into a fit of laughter, smacking the table with her hand so loudly that people are turning in their seats to take a look at us.

"Shh," I tell her, but she can't stop laughing.

"I'm sorry." She's wiping tears from the corner of her eyes. "I should've been there to stay your hand."

I groan and flop my head in my hands, because I'm an adult and should've been able to *stay* my own hand, but it would've helped if Monica had texted me back right away. Then I tell her about my run-in at the barn with Michael and before I even finish, she's saying, "Girl, uh-uh, we are *done* with him. He can't be treating you like that, not after everything you been through." She gulps her venti white chocolate mocha—no whip, half-caff, half almond milk, half coconut—and then she leans forward and says, "What are we going to do now? Revenge plot? Payback? Rebound? Where are we at?"

I roll my eyes. "None of that, it's fine—"

"It's not fine, Mila, and what kind of friend would I be if I just sat back and let your boy break up with you without any payback?"

I smile and shake my head. "You saying that is enough for me."

She's scrolling through her phone and a minute later goes, "What about this guy?" And it's one of her cousins or someone connected to her family somehow. "You don't have to, like, *date him* date him. You could just go out, snuggle up, and I could take pictures and we post them all over. Yeah?"

"Mon, I'm okay, really." I consider telling her about Alex, but decide there's nothing really to tell, so I keep it to myself. "Tell me about you. How was your break?"

Over the Christmas break, Monica had gone with her latest boy toy on a Caribbean cruise. Her parents thought she was on a study abroad trip—in no way would they endorse such a holiday. Monica grew up in a very strict Catholic household—no sleepovers, no parties, no boyfriends, nada. In many ways we could relate, but whereas I mostly toed the line, Monica went off the deep end when we got to college. And I was always there to hold back her hair, pick up the pieces of her failed relationships, and generally play the role of wing woman. Between Anya and me, I was always the wild one, but between Mon and me, I'm about as tame as they come.

As she regales me with the ups and downs of her cruise—a disastrous excursion where she and Roberto got into a huge fight, a fortuitous round of Blackjack in the ship's casino, and quite a few "lively" dinners (whatever *that* means, I'm too afraid to ask). However, when they hit the shore, Monica broke up with him posthaste, claiming the trip proved they were incompatible.

"Why can't I just find a male version of you?" she moans.

"Hmm, don't think they make men like me."

"I'm not giving up hope." She puts her hands on the table in front of me, palms up, clearly wanting me to put my hands in hers. I sigh and oblige her. "So really, what can we do? Makeover?" She inspects my fingernails. "At the very least you need a manicure."

"You're the only one in the world who cares what my fingers look like, Mon."

"Doubtful."

I laugh, because I'm pretty sure Monica really thinks having a decent mani/pedi will change my fortunes with Michael. Eventually, I let her cajole me into going to her favorite spot in Coral Gables. We stop at a hole-in-the-wall Cuban bakery on our way and pick up guava and cheese pastries and cafe con leches despite being overly caffeinated already.

"Just so you know, my nails will be chipped by tomorrow," I tell Monica as we pick out nail polish colors.

"Horse people problems." She sighs dramatically. "*Endless* horse people problems."

Even though I was reluctant to go, the outing does improve my spirits and makes me feel like maybe there is hope for Michael and me. It won't be as easy as changing my nail color, but part of me is beginning to think if I can change some things, Michael might take me back. As I sit back in the pedicure massage chair while the aesthetician scrubs at my heels, I think about what I can say to Michael to convince him I can change. I don't come up with any revolutionary ideas, but I do start to hope.

On Thursday at the barn, after I flat Cyrus, I walk into Trina's office to see if there are any other horses I can ride for her. Standing in her office, huddled around her desk, is Alex. Trina and Alex are whispering frantically about something, and when I walk in, they straighten up and stop talking.

Which doesn't make me feel awkward, at all.

"Uh," I start, looking between them. "Just seeing who else still needs to be hacked."

Trina doesn't miss a beat, the little sneak, and says, "Norah and JoJo both need to get their willies out." She turns back to Alex and seemingly continues on with their former conversation. "What I was saying about the bedding is that I like the price point of the pellets better..."

I nod and walk out, but I know for sure they weren't whispering about *shavings* before I walked in. They were talking about me. But what, exactly—and why—I'm not sure.

On Friday, we're back at WEF. After a killer class, where Cyrus and I had the fastest time in the jump off by two whole seconds, I'm walking around the vendors with a frozen lemonade alongside Trina.

There is something amazing about being in a place where every shop consists of people who are just as horse-crazy as you. There's horse *everything* amongst the vendors at WEF—scarves with horses, purses with bits, socks with every kind of horse-adjacent thing you can think of. There's a vendor who will paint a portrait of your horse and frame it for ten thousand dollars. Diamond horseshoe necklaces and bracelets where you can get your horse's name engraved on a plaque.

Trina and I are eating it all up. If I had unlimited funds, this is where I'd spend it.

It takes me back to this time last year, before Anya's first and last Grand Prix, when my mom, Anya, and I were walking through the vendors, tugging my dad along after us.

"I would save more money if we went on a shopping spree at Neiman Marcus," my dad muttered under his breath.

"Is that an offer for a shopping spree?" Anya teased.

"You get through this crazy business you've got going today, and you can have a shopping spree anywhere," my dad said. Of course, Anya didn't get through it, and we never did get our shopping spree.

A little while later, Trina and I are discussing the class, and she's try-ing—yet again—to convince me to move up to the High Amateur Jumper division. I'm rebuffing her, though without the same inner vehemence as before. Could that be a way for me to prove myself to Michael? To show him that I can change?

We're roving from stall to stall, hovering at a shop with tiny porcelain figurines of horses and other animals. After a moment of silence, I change the subject. "You and Alex seem to know each other well." I say it as a way of eventually getting at what they were whispering about yesterday in the barn, but her answer surprises me so much that I don't even remember my original intention.

"I dated his cousin for a while." She says it matter-of-factly, but there's something about her tone that seems to say, *Don't question me anymore about this.*

"Where's his cousin now?" I ask anyway.

She sighs and sets down a figurine of a Jack Russell. "Cuba."

"Oh. How did...I mean, did you...uh, how'd he get there?"

"Deported."

"I see." And then I'm flashing back to my kiss with Alex as the Im-migration police stood only feet away. In another universe, Alex might be in Cuba right now, too. A ribbon of worry coils in me as I think of the possibility of Alex getting deported. I try to shove it to the side, to tell myself I only care as a friend and nothing more. But the worry is still there, slithering around in my stomach.

"Did you—"

"It ended badly. That's all that can be said."

"Okay," I say, drawing out the word. It's not like Trina to be so curt, but then again, she's never been very forthcoming about her personal stuff. So maybe I shouldn't be surprised. "And then Alex...?"

She glances up at the sky, as if she needs divine intervention for this conversation. "I was...around, when Alex's dad passed. I knew Alex and his mom needed help, so I offered what I could."

"That was nice of you."

"Yeah, it is." And the way she says it, I know that's the end of the conversation. And I'm dying to know the whole story.

The next day, I'm driving to the show when Trina calls me. "Where are you?" she's practically shouting into the phone.

"I just got off the Turnpike, about ten minutes away. Why? What's up?"

"A pipe burst in the DeNemethy ring so they changed your class to the International Arena. They're walking the course right now."

"What?! Trina, why am I hearing about this now?"

"Well, if you checked your phone you'd know about it."

"I'm driving! I have that thing that my dad made me do, where the phone shuts off your texts when you drive."

"Daddy Big Bucks strikes again." She sighs. "Look, I'll send you a picture of the course and I'll get a couple videos of the first few riders on course. Just get here and get Cyrus, I'll move you as far back in the order as I can."

"Okay," I say, though I don't feel okay. "Thanks, Trina."

"Sure thing, chica. Drive safe."

When I get to the showground and finally check my texts, sure enough there's a litany of messages from Trina about my class getting changed around. I also notice a few texts from Alex—which means Trina must have given him my number. I can't help but feel shaky, like I've just downed three Red Bulls. By the time I arrive at the temporary barns, Alex already has Cyrus tacked up on the cross-ties.

"Hey!" he says, a little too loudly. He seems like he's a little too hyped up on caffeine, too. It's almost like he's vibrating, and it's just making me more anxious. "You excited? International Arena! That's exciting. I would be excited."

"Excited. Right."

"It's okay to be nervous, it's a new place. Why don't you sit down and look at the videos Trina sent you?"

"Alright." I don't know how to deal with this jumpy version of Alex, but I do as he suggests and take a seat just outside the barns and watch the videos. They're from a weird angle—on the opposite side of the in-gate, which seems strange for Trina to walk all that way to film for me. Trina is talking to me in the videos, giving me her tips for how to get Cyrus through the course—take this turn, push him for the five strides instead of six, slow him through this line, etc. The jumps seem massive, and the ring is sprawling.

And, of course, it's the site of Anya's accident. A truth I can't shake as I watch the videos again and again.

By the time I'm confident I've got the course memorized, I watch the videos a couple more times, but it doesn't do anything to calm my nerves. I've studied the distances, counting the horses' strides as they gallop through the course, thought through every single turn, every individual stride. Trina always says, *Control what you can control and forget about the rest.* I'm trying to do that, but I can only control my mind so much. There's one jump near the in-gate that's close to where Anya had her accident, and it's that singular jump that's freaking me out the most. It's not even that spectacular of a jump—it's a regular blue and white oxer with normal standards, though it does seem really huge. All the jumps do. Of course it could just be that everything seems bigger in the International Arena, but a part of me wonders if they forgot to lower the jumps from the previous class.

But no, they wouldn't do that.

"C'mon, Mila, get yourself together," I mumble.

"Ready?" Alex says as he approaches with Cyrus.

"As I'll ever be."

He helps me into the saddle and then walks beside me as we go to the Arena. He's practically bouncing on his toes, and Cyrus is doing his typical prancing horse routine, while I silently clench my teeth and try to review the course in my mind. Alex seems to get that I don't want to talk, so he's whistling. *Whistling.* Since when does Alex whistle? I don't really know who spiked his coffee this morning, but I'm not sure I like this peppy Alex.

At the practice ring, Trina already has a jump set up for us, so I immediately start warming him up. The exercise gives me calm—I can't think about the course or the arena as Cyrus and I weave around the other horses. At first, Cyrus is really fresh and he's tossing his head, kicking out his back legs and chomping at the bit. But eventually the jitters wear off and we're jumping higher and higher practice fences until they're almost the height of the standards. Then Trina is waving me over to the in-gate.

"You're in," she says.

"What?" She normally gives me time to watch a rider or two before me, but all of a sudden, I'm in the ring. My heart is booming in my chest and I'm certain everyone in the entire stadium can hear it. I'm trotting toward the spot where Anya last moved her whole body, and then I'm cantering past it and it's behind me.

"Next on course in our High Amateur Jumpers we have Cyrus Van Der Bergh, ridden and owned by Miss Mila Kozak of Miami, Florida." For a second, I think I've misheard the announcer—*High* Amateur Jumpers? This is supposed to be the Low Amateur Jumpers. But when I look up at the scoreboard, where Cyrus and I are being projected live, I see it clear as day: High Amateur Jumper, Mila Kozak, Cyrus Van Der Bergh.

My whole body is shaking, and I'm about to turn Cyrus around and get out of this arena, undo this mistake or whatever this is, when the buzzer shrieks. And, as always, Cyrus bursts into a gallop at the sound.

Just like that, we are on course. In the High Amateur Jumpers in the International Arena, jumping the same jumps, the same heights as Anya did right before she fell and lost all movement in her body.

My stomach is roiling, bile threatening to burn my throat. I swallow it down and, with quivering hands, point Cyrus toward the first jump. Just one jump, I tell myself. We'll just jump one jump.

It's a black vertical with huge yellow arches underneath the top pole. And when I say it's huge, that's like saying a Clydesdale's hooves are moderately sized. But then we're soaring over it, and I tell myself, just *one* more jump. I can do one more jump.

Cyrus and I gallop through the turn into a five stride line. We hit the five perfectly, and then we're making a tight rollback toward a plank jump. We leave a bit long, and I fall onto Cyrus's neck as we land, but we both recover and the jump is still standing, even though I'm quite literally shaking in my boots.

*One more jump. One more jump.*

The next obstacles are arguably the hardest in the course—the triple combination. Cyrus is absolutely flying, so I sit back and rein him in as we approach. We zoom through, a perfect staccato as we jump one after the other after the other.

At some point in the course, I stop telling myself *one more jump*. Because despite the fear quaking through my body, I want to finish the course. I want it more than anything I've ever wanted in my life. It grips me tighter than the fear, and propels me to the next jump and the next.

There's an option after the triple—we can either jump a very high, very skinny vertical or go over the water jump. I choose the water, and let Cyrus gallop full-tilt toward it. His whole body expands underneath me as I extend my arms as far as they can go up his neck.

We are winged. We are flying. We won't ever touch the ground.

And then, we do. And we're hurtling toward the green Adequan jump. We're shooting through a broken line, and we take the inside for six strides. It's a bit tight and at the last minute, Cyrus inserts an extra half-stride before taking off. He gives a valiant effort to get over the fence, but his hooves graze the top, and I can tell the rail falls because I hear the crowd go, "Ahh."

I should feel disappointed, but honestly, I'm just happy we got over it and we're still alive. We're speeding over an orange Hermés jump and then one of those obnoxiously huge butterfly fences before turning to the final jump: the blue and white oxer near Anya's spot. I sit back, collecting Cyrus as much as I can. I'm gripping the reins like they're the only thing holding me to this earth. We thunder toward it, and I'm holding my breath, and then his feet are off the ground. We're sailing over it, gliding through the air like this is what we were made to do, and then we land.

We've finished the course, and we're both still whole.

Trina and Alex are at the in-gate, cheering, their matching, conspiratorial smiles tell me all I need to know: they planned this. They tricked me. I don't know whether to be upset with them or giddy.

It hits me that I could've been hurt—badly. I could've ended up like Anya. A tiny flare of anger sparks in my chest. What were they thinking, springing this on me like that? What if something bad had happened? Or what if I got in there, realized what was happening, and turned around and left like an idiot? They could have embarrassed me in front of everyone.

But then I see Trina's smile, Alex's dancing brown eyes, and I decide to choose to be giddy, because, well, I can't help it. I just jumped Grand Prix-level jumps—and I survived. More than survived. I thrived.

Trina's saying something, slapping my leg as she feeds Cyrus a treat. And as much as I want to pay attention to her feedback, I'm looking at Alex. I'm watching his eyes shine as he rubs Cyrus's mane and smiles up at me.

I cut off Trina. "Thank you, guys," I say. "I wouldn't have done this without you."

"Uh, yeah, we know. That's why we did this," Trina says, with a wave of her hand. "We knew you were capable, you just needed a little...push."

I laugh, though I wouldn't categorize this as a *little* push. "Fair enough."

"You deserve to get through your fear," Alex says in that amiable way of his.

It's a profound thing to say, and I feel like I should say something equally profound back, but no words come to me. So I just smile and nod. Trina hands me some water and I down it in one gulp. I'm shivering, not from cold, but from the let-down of adrenaline from the course. Cyrus is picking up on it, because he's prancing again, even as I give him the reins and he lets his head down.

I'm filled then by the exhilaration of what we just did, and I let it consume me. The sheer terror of jumping those heights combine with the unbelievable thrill of accomplishing something so outlandish. Waves of emotion—gratitude, elation, relief—crash over me and I'm taken out by them.

I'm so caught up in my feelings that when Alex asks me to dinner, I say yes.

# Chapter Eight

# Hurricane Mila

I shower at Trina's and then meet Alex back at the barn. He offered to pick me up, but I didn't want any comments from Trina. I'm regretting that I agreed to dinner, especially as my plan to win back Michael is finally taking shape in my mind. I resolve to make it clear that this is dinner as *friends*, but when I see Alex standing by his car waiting for me, the thought flees from my mind.

He's never looked so good in a pair of tapered chinos and a white shirt topped with a dark leather bomber jacket. He's got a five o'clock shadow cropping up, and the black hair contrasts nicely with his tan skin. And, to top it all off, he's holding a bundle of yellow tulips in brown floral paper.

So much for *just friends*.

We hug, a little awkwardly, probably because neither of us is sure what it is we're doing here. He opens the passenger door for me and my heart goes nuts like I'm back on course, and I'm just thinking, *What am I doing here?*

I get my phone out and quickly text Monica: *I'm on a date by accident, what should I do??* I stash the phone in my purse as Alex climbs into the car.

"Where're we off to?" I ask because I don't know what else to say.

"You'll see," he says with a quirk of his mouth, and then I'm thinking about our kiss and feeling a flush from head to toe.

*Get it together, Mila.*

We drive in uncomfortable silence for several minutes until Alex turns on some music. Nicky Youre's song "Sunroof" comes on and suddenly we're both singing along.

"I love this song!"

Alex's half-smile breaks into the full deal and he turns up the song even louder and lowers the windows. We're both singing at the top of our lungs, my hand out the window, catching the breeze as we drive.

When the song fades, things are more normal between us and we're reliving the class from earlier.

"Oh man, that triple was wow, I don't even have words—"

"Perfection?"

"Yeah, maybe even better than perfection."

"That's what it seemed like." He pauses, as if he's considering his words, then says, "I'm proud of you, Mila."

"For what? You guys forced me into that class."

"You always have a choice. You could've left."

"Maybe. I realized it right before the buzzer, but Cyrus always jumps at the sound and takes off. I didn't have much of a choice." I shrug. "But in a way I'm happy the choice was taken from me. I don't think I would've done it otherwise."

"I think you would've. It just might have taken a while."

"It's nice that you think that."

"Sometimes you just have to borrow other people's faith in you."

"I like that. Did your therapist tell you that, too?"

"No," he laughs. "I came up with that all on my own."

"I'm impressed."

"Then it's working."

"What is?"

"My plan to impress you."

I snort-laugh. "Your plan's a bit risky so far—forcing me into a class I didn't want to be in? That could've seriously backfired."

"That's true, but I was willing to take that risk to help you."

"Hmm."

Alex leans closer to me. "Impressed yet?"

I try to hold back a smile, but fail. "Maybe."

"I'll take it."

We end up at a trendy place called Maxwell's Plum, with marble tables, velvet chairs, gold accents, and bold wallpaper. I feel stylish just by being here. As we're escorted to our table by the hostess, Alex puts his hand on my lower back. It feels like there's lightning in his touch, as if a million bolts of electricity are pinging off of his fingers onto my back. I'm out of sorts by the time we reach our seats, and I can't look him in the eye as I pretend to read the menu.

"Have you been here before?" I ask as casually as I can manage.

"No," Alex says, looking up from his menu. "I've been waiting for a good reason."

A cramp of guilt hitches in my stomach—I don't want to be his good reason, because I don't want to ruin this for him. I don't respond and we go back to reading our menus. A waiter appears beside us, startling me. I give a little jump in my seat, and my insides feel as if Cyrus is galloping all through me. The waiter gives us the specials and recommends some wines for us to try. Alex orders something to drink, asks if I want the same, and I nod, even though I couldn't hear what he was saying with my nerves thundering in my ears.

"Can we get some bread?" Alex requests. The waiter leaves, and he says, "If I know you, you haven't eaten today, have you?"

"Not...really," I confess, surprised that Alex knows this about me.

"Have you always been that way with shows? Or is it just since Anya's accident?" He says it so matter-of-factly—the way that no one else will—and it cuts a jab to my heart. *Anya*. She would like Alex, I think. She would approve of me going on this date. Not that it's a *date*, I remind myself.

"I've always had a hard time eating before competitions, even when I was in Little League soccer, but Anya's accident definitely amplified it."

He nods. "I know it's not the same, but I had a really hard time driving after my dad died."

"He died in a car accident?"

"From complications after the accident."

"I'm so sorry."

"Thank you." I notice he doesn't say 'It's okay' like some people do when you say, 'I'm sorry.' It's the second time he's done this and it strikes me as very intentional. "That was actually one of the first times I've driven with the music so loud since he passed."

"In the car? Just now?"

He nods.

"Wow."

"Healing takes time," he says quietly.

I run my fingers across the glossy marble table. "I believe you."

"You don't think you've healed, do you?"

A very ladylike snort comes out of me.

"You have. I mean, even the fact that you're competing on Cyrus shows that you're healing."

"A buffoon would show Cyrus."

"You always have a choice, Mila."

It's true, and I want to take credit for making that decision, but of course I can't.

The waiter arrives with the bread and serves us a white wine. The fruity, alcoholic scent wafts over the table and just one sniff of it makes me feel lightheaded.

"Hey, can I ask you something?" I'm lathering butter on a piece of bread as Alex sips the wine.

"Of course."

"What's the deal with Trina and your cousin?"

He sets down his glass, his lips pressing together into a straight line. "I don't think that's my story to tell."

"Trina told me they dated, and he got deported."

Alex sighs, rubbing his hand across the back of his neck. "Yeah, that's the short version."

"And the long one?" I stuff the buttered bread into my mouth.

He fixes me with a look like it's none of my business, but he continues anyway. "They dated for a long time. I definitely thought they were going to get married. But then my cousin got into some crazy Ponzi-type scheme and he got arrested. Trina offered to marry him to keep him from getting deported, but he turned her down. He's back in Cuba now."

"Whoa," I say with my mouth still half full. "He turned her down? That's...rough."

"Yeah, I was honestly amazed when she offered my mom and me help after my dad died."

I nod, digesting what he's told me. It certainly explains why Trina hasn't dated at all, or at least not publicly, while I've known her. It also makes sense why she's been such an advocate for losing myself in the horses since my Breakup—she did the same. There's no one I know who's as singularly focused on horses as Trina.

I wonder distantly if everyone gets a happy ending eventually. Will Trina? Or is her success on horseback her version of a happily ever after? I think of my parents, Anya, me. Will we get our happy endings? Anya's accident has made me feel like fate is a wily backstabber, but that doesn't necessarily mean the story's over. I want to hope, to believe the best is yet to come, but I'm not convinced.

The waiter comes back to get our orders. I really want the Miso Salmon, but it's one of the more expensive things on the menu. And I definitely don't want to break Alex's wallet *and* his heart in one night. So I order the Rigatoni Primavera, even though I'm not totally sure what it is, but the price point is better than the salmon. Alex orders the Plum Burger, the cheapest entree on the menu, and my heart twinges.

Before I can say what I want to say—that we're just friends, it can't go farther than just this—Alex starts telling me about his black hole book that he just finished reading.

"Basically, most black holes are formed from a star that's run out of energy and it dies. A star, like our sun, is powered by a ton of nuclear fusion, but once there's no more energy for the atoms to fuse, it's like it becomes too heavy for itself and it collapses under its own weight. But stars are huge, right? And even though they're collapsing, their mass stays the same. So that means there's a crazy amount of mass in a teeny tiny space—"

"It's super dense."

Alex's eyes twinkle at my remark, and there's something about it that makes my stomach flip. "That's exactly right. And the more dense something is, the greater the gravitational pull. Eventually the gravity in that collapsed star is so intense that not even light can escape from it. And if you get too close, you get pulled into the black hole because its gravitational pull is so strong—" Alex stops short. "Am I boring you?"

"No, not at all. I've never even thought about black holes before, but it just seems like..." I trail off, trying to find the words for what I'm feeling.

"Like an analogy for life?"

"Yeah, actually it does. Like there's this tragedy—the star dies," or, Anya is paralyzed, "and then it collapses in on itself," AKA my whole world falls apart, "and the tragedy pulls everything around it into the disaster."

"Exactly."

"So then, how do you avoid it?"

"Disaster in general, or black holes?"

"Aren't they the same?"

"Touché."

"So, how do you get out of a black hole?"

Alex takes a sip of his wine, and I can tell he's debating whether he should tell me or not. "You can't," he finally says. "Once you get pulled in, it's called spaghettification. The black hole strings you out like spaghetti."

"Stop."

"I'm dead serious."

"I don't believe you."

"Look it up."

I quirk an eyebrow, but don't make a move toward my phone. "Okay, so let's just say I believe you. What happens after you're spaghetticafied? Spaghettified?" I shake my head, because there's no way that's a thing.

"Well, it's all theoretical, right? If it's a big black hole, you just keep floating through the darkness until you get to the singularity. Then, you cease to exist." He shrugs, because what else can you say to that? "Your best bet is to stay away from the event horizon—that's the point of no return."

"I see." And I'm just wondering, where am I in this analogy? Am I past the point of no return? Can I never go back to who I was before Anya's accident? Or am I floating on the edge of the event horizon, still able to be salvaged?

"But," Alex says, "to answer your real question, I think when you're in a proverbial black hole in your life, sometimes you need someone on the other side to drag you out."

I'm sitting there, fork hovering inches off my plate, with Alex's eyes heavy on me, and I'm suddenly feeling so exposed; so very, very vulnerable. Because who's going to drag me out? I would've thought that person was Michael—my boyfriend of *two years*—but that's not going great at the moment. Considering my next best option—Anya—*is* the singularity, that's not happening. But the way Alex is looking at me, I just can't handle it right now. So I do the only thing I can do in this moment—I change the subject. So fast I think Alex might have whiplash.

"Did you see that Tom Cruise movie?"

For a second, Alex looks confused, and then he says, slowly, "Are you talking about *Top Gun?*"

"Yeah, that one."

He's shaking his head, but he's got a smile playing on his lips, so I think I've gotten away with my subject change. "I think you're the only one in North America who would refer to it as 'that Tom Cruise movie,' but yes, I did see it. Did you?"

"Not really. I fell asleep like thirty minutes in," I tell him as I stab at my pasta.

He laughs, and it makes me feel jittery inside. "You might be the singular person in all of existence who could say that."

"I'm special like that." I shrug. I'm wondering if there's such a thing as trauma-induced narcolepsy. Because I may not be able to fall asleep at night in my bed, but I sure can fall asleep just about anywhere else.

Between bites of creamy pasta, we connect over a movie we both loathed that was a huge hit a few years ago.

"I saw that same actress in a movie where she played someone with cerebral palsy and I swear she acted the exact same way."

"Oh, she didn't have cerebral palsy in the other one? Could've fooled me." He's laughing, and I'm beginning to think he has the best laugh I've ever heard. That's when I realize I've probably had too much wine and I push my glass away.

A couple named Cat and Carlos are playing live music. He's playing guitar and harmonizing as she sings an acoustic version of Shawn Mendes' "There's Nothing Holding Me Back." It's beautiful and heart-breaking at the same time—their rendition has so much raw passion in it that it almost brings tears to my eyes.

I ask him about his experience immigrating to the U.S. It turns out that we both came to the States when we were in elementary school—I was in third grade, he was in fifth.

"I was so painfully shy," Alex says, "they didn't think I could speak English, even though I could. They put me in ESOL for two years before someone connected the dots that I was *writing* in English just fine."

"Oh my gosh." I shake my head. "That's terrible."

"Yeah, well, I should've spoken up."

"Alex, you were a kid. That's not your fault."

"Maybe," he says. "But I feel better when I'm in control of the trajectory of my life. And being bitter about some teacher I barely remember, that feels petty. I should've spoken up." He takes a sip of his wine and then tilts the glass toward me. "What about you?"

"Coming to the States felt like...like I just got thrust into that board game Candyland. You remember that one?"

He nods. "I was always getting stuck in that chocolate swamp."

"Right? But it's kind of like Candyland here. Everything's so bright, so colorful, so *much*. You have so many options—I mean, the *food*." I laugh. "People don't realize how many choices we have here. Anything you can *think* of, it exists. I literally gained like twenty pounds one year"—once my dad started making money and we could actually buy what seemed like all the food in the world. "My parents put me in soccer because they wanted me to run it all off."

"Chunky Mila? That's hard to imagine."

"I was still cute," I say, flipping my hair over my shoulder.

"Oh now that's easy to believe." And he's got a glint in his eye that's making me feel unsteady.

I glance away, pushing my empty plate to the center of the table. Cat and Carlos are now singing Jewel's "You Were Meant For Me" and for the first time since we got here, I'm thinking about Michael. I go to grab my phone out of my purse to add this song to my Breakup playlist, but then a group of waiters and waitresses come around the corner singing the restaurant's version of "Happy Birthday." Our waiter is carrying a plate of rose cake with 'Happy Birthday' written on the plate with a fruity dessert sauce. And, of course, there's a pair of sparklers in the cake, flames dancing above the dessert. The waiter places it in front of me and I glance up at Alex, bewildered, and he's just laughing hysterically at me. Around the restaurant, everyone is clapping along to the song. I feel their eyes on me, on Alex. They probably think we're a couple. A happy one at that.

Once the waiters clear out, I glare at him. "You know very well it's not my birthday."

He's laughing so hard he's got tears leaking out of the sides of his eyes. "I know, but that look on your face was so worth it."

"I'm not sharing this with you," I say as I take a bite of the cake. It's unlike anything I've ever tasted, delicate and moist. "Oh wow. I'm definitely not sharing."

"We'll see about that." He gets up from his side of the table and swings his chair right next to me, spoon outstretched toward the dessert. I grab the spoon from his hand, but he's not letting go, and then we're wrestling over the spoon, laughing. He wraps an arm around me, taking hold of my other arm so that I can't grab at him anymore. We're all tangled up, quivering with laughter, when we both become very aware of how close we are. Alex is looking in my eyes, his face inches from mine, and then his eyes are on my mouth. Before he can move any closer, I pull away.

"Fine, I'll share," I say as I push the cake toward him, my heart beating erratically.

After we finish off the cake, the band is playing "More Than Words" by Extreme. I'm feeling skittish—I keep thinking of the way Alex's eyes were on me, staring at my lips. And I know he wanted to kiss me. And of course it's my fault because I can't say what I know I need to say.

"I would ask you to dance," Alex says coyly, "except I'm pretty sure you owe me a dance. So, it's time to pay up, Miss Kozak."

Just as the duet is singing the perfect line for this moment, Alex is taking my hand and leading me close to where the band is playing in the corner of the restaurant.

He pulls me in, but not too close, and I'm grateful he's not pushing it too far. One of my hands is still in his hand, the other is around his back. We're swaying in time with the strumming of the guitar as the music washes over us.

While I'm in his arms, it's easy to forget that I don't want to be here. Easy to pretend that this is a thing—that we're a couple. For a moment, I let myself believe the lie. Let myself give in to how good it feels to be with Alex.

As the song goes on, we get closer; his cheek is pressing against my temple and I can feel his chest rising and falling with each breath he takes. It's rhythmic, lulling me into a comfortability that I don't actually feel.

The song ends and the lead singer says, "I adore seeing lovebirds on the dance floor," nodding toward Alex and me.

Alex is smiling down at me in that shy way of his, but my entire body feels like it's on fire and I'm sure everyone can sense the red hot embarrassment coming off of me in waves. I want to walk away—no, I want to *run* away—but Alex is keeping me in place with his arm around my waist.

The band starts playing "Crash into Me" and somehow we keep dancing. He moves my hand onto his chest, and beneath my palm I feel his heart beating in triple time. In a way, I'm glad I'm not the only one totally losing it right now. On the other hand, *What am I doing?* My chest feels like it's going to collapse in on me with all the chaos going on in there.

I put my head on his chest, and can't help but inhale his sandalwood scent. My whole body is tingling with the newness, the electricity of this dance; it feels like each of the molecules in my body are evaporating one by one. At the end of the night, I'll cease to be.

I know I'm in love with Michael, but I can't deny what's happening here with Alex—there's fireworks at every point we're touching. I tell myself it's only because we kissed, I wouldn't have felt this way if we hadn't had that experience. Even as I tell myself that, my body is betraying my heart and mind, but I can feel them following suit, too.

Alex spins me, and when he guides me back toward him, our faces are so close, they're almost touching. And then he's inching closer, and I'm frozen. By fear, by guilt, by the electricity that's coursing through my veins. But when his lips are almost to mine, I tug away. "I can't," I say. And, like the coward I am, I run.

I have no idea how long I'm in the bathroom for, but once I'm done hyperventilating, I realize I *have* to come out. I mean, I can't spend the night in here. I call Monica five times in a row, but she doesn't pick up. I debate ordering an Uber and bypassing Alex, but I know I'll have to face him at some point at the barn, and leaving like that will just make it all worse.

He's sitting back at our table, and I can't look him in the eye when I say, "I'm sorry, Alex."

He glances up at me, and I expect to see wounded eyes, but he's shuttered up like Category 5 Hurricane Mila just blew through. And, honestly, that's worse. I feel like total crap, because Alex is a good guy and under different circumstances, this night would've gone way differently. He doesn't say anything—not 'it's okay,' or 'I get it.' He just sort of dips his head in a nod and stands up.

"Ready to go?" he asks. He doesn't wait for my response. He knows I want to leave. But as he's walking away, I have this overwhelming feeling that I'm ruining something really good. So I grab his arm.

"Alex?"

"Yeah?" My heart drops when I see the hope in his eyes before he quickly hardens them again.

"Can we be friends?" And it sounds so pathetic, even to my ears, that I'm sure he's just going to laugh at me, or leave me at Maxwell's Plum to order that Uber.

"Sure, Mila." His voice is so resigned, it shatters my already damaged heart. And, as we walk out of the restaurant, I'm sure everyone in here can see the trail of destruction I'm leaving in my wake.

# Chapter Nine

---

# Oh Mi-ami

O n Monday after my classes, I actually go to the library and work on my essay. For the first time, it seems to flow, and at the end of my session, I even email a rough draft to Natasha. Not to write, but to edit. I meet up with Monica for lunch, and she goes full-on Bad Cop on me as she interrogates me about my 'accidental date.' I forgot that I had texted her, and I got back so late last night that I didn't even check my texts—pretty much a first for me.

"Who is this guy? How in the world do you end up on an accidental date? And what were you doing instead of texting me back?"

I blush, and she goes berserk.

"Oh, Mi-ami," Monica says, a classic saying of hers. "WHO IS THIS GUY, MILA?! You're blushing! You're really blushing! What did you do with him? Oh no, what did he do with you?"

"Calm down, calm down. I don't know exactly how it happened—he asked me to dinner and I said yes, but I wasn't really thinking it was going to be a date—"

"What did you think it was gonna be? A study group?"

"I know, it seems naive now—"

"Ya think?"

"But we're friends. I dunno, we've gone out before, like in groups, but never like this."

"So where did you go? What did you do? Did he pay? Did he kiss you?"

I laugh and shake my head. This is one of the many reasons I love Monica. As many times as I've been her wing woman, she's mine, too.

"Well, it's a little complicated..." and then I finally tell her about my kiss with Alex when Immigration came to WEF.

"How are you just now telling me about this? Mila, this is it. This is your way over Michael. Rub it in his Baywatch face. He deserves it, the little *tarado*."

"That's not what I want. I don't want to use Alex like that."

"Oh my gosh, you really like him."

I shrug. "He's just a good guy."

"*Just* a good guy doesn't make you blush like that."

"He *is* a good kisser."

"I'm sorry, explain to me why you're not dating him already?"

"I'm in love with Michael," I mumble. "I want to be with him, I want to get him back."

"Right, and that's why you're making out with hot guys and out dancing with them till the middle of the night."

"It's not like that. Besides, it ended in total disaster. He went to kiss me and I freaked out."

Monica shakes her head, like she's really disappointed in me, and there's a part of me that's a little disappointed in myself, too. After lunch, we head back to the library and work on our homework, but I keep thinking about what Monica said—if I really loved Michael that much, would I have kissed Alex like that? Even if it was to save him, would I have even thought of it? The idea bothers me, and I can't seem to focus, so after an hour of time-wasting, I pack up and head to the barn. I had been trying so hard not to think of the failed date all day long, but talking to Monica blew that plan to bits. So now I'm gripping the steering wheel, navigating the Turnpike at eighty-five miles an hour, my whole body tense as I curse myself for this mess I've gotten into.

At Trina's, it's breezy and cool, the wind carrying the scent of wood-kilned shavings with it. And let me just tell you, there is no perfume better in the world than fresh shavings on a cool day. You can keep your Chanel No.5; give me a stall full of shavings and a warm horse any day of the week. Add a little Eau de Alfalfa on top of that, and this girl is set. Being at the barn settles me in a way that nothing else can. I know that Cyrus will love me, no matter who I offended last night. And that's enough for me. At least for right now.

To my surprise, I find Michael tacking up Khan, which must mean he's not avoiding me anymore.

"Hey," he says as he stands up from picking Khan's feet.

"Hey," I say, and somehow I feel like he can see clearly that I kissed Alex, that I went out with him on Sunday, that I'm thinking about Alex and not just Michael.

"I was hoping to run into you."

"Oh yeah?" I try to sound casual, like it's no big deal he wanted to see me, but my heart is in my throat—along with my stomach, liver, and every other important organ in my body.

"I heard about the High Amateurs."

"Yeah...it was crazy."

"I'm proud of you. I know that must've been hard." His blue eyes are soft and bright—they look the way they've looked a thousand times before. Like they love me, like they belong only to me. And it's this look that solidifies the plan that has been forming in my mind for days now. An utterly outrageous plan that anyone with half a brain would veto immediately.

"Thanks." And then I blurt, "I'm thinking about doing the Grand Prix this weekend." Yep, *that*, ladies and gentlemen, is my grand plan to win Michael back.

"Oh wow."

"I was thinking about what you said." I step closer to him. "I don't want to stay this way, Michael. I want to change. I want to be the girl you fell in love with." *And obviously competing in one of the deadliest sports in the world will prove that to you.*

His eyes are darting back and forth over mine, and it's like he's trying to figure out if I'm serious about this. "I want that, too." His voice is low and raspy, like it gets when he's about to kiss me.

"Really?" There is so much hope and desperation in my voice, but I don't even care because Michael just said he wants me back. Or, at least, that's what I *think* he's saying.

"Yeah, I do."

I take another step closer to him, but as I do, he turns away to continue saddling Khan. My stomach drops as if I've just taken a fall, and I want more than anything for him to turn back to me. I want it so much that I say, "If I compete on Sunday, will you come watch me?"

He glances up at me as he's pulling up Khan's girth, and smiles. But it's a sad smile, as if he pities me, or maybe he thinks I'm lying. And maybe I am. "Of course," he says, and just like that, wings of hope are beating a rhythm in my chest. "And then, I dunno, maybe we could go out after? Just to, y'know, celebrate?"

"Sure," I squeak out. And then, because I can't stand my own desperation, I walk away to Cyrus's stall, where I lock myself inside. I curl into myself in the corner, my head on my knees, as I force myself to take deep breaths. I remind myself that *this* is what I wanted: a chance to show Michael I'm still Mila—the Mila he fell in love with. And I'm decidedly closer to that goal.

But, the panic ripping through my chest is telling me something else. Because even though I may be one step closer to winning over Michael, I also may have just signed my death warrant.

Later, when I tell Trina what I want to do, she's shocked. "Are you sure?" It's supposed to be her day off, but because she's Trina, she's at the barn anyway.

"Isn't this what you wanted for me?" I say slowly.

"Well, yeah, of course, but is this what *you* want?"

"Yeah it is." I may not *want* to ride in a Grand Prix, but I definitely want to win Michael back. And maybe it'll be like the High Amateurs—once I'm there, I'll *want* to be there.

"You and Cyrus are definitely capable. I mean, he *is* a Grand Prix horse and you are a very capable rider. I'm supportive."

I exhale loudly. Even though I was pretty sure Trina would approve, I wasn't one hundred percent sure, and I thought there was a chance she'd see through my thin motivations.

Maybe she does, but maybe she's okay with it.

We come up with a schooling plan for the week and then register for the classes for the weekend. Since I competed on Cyrus yesterday, I give him a break and ride a couple of the lesson horses who aren't going to WEF this season.

I don't see Alex at all, which leaves me with a bittersweet feeling. I made definitive progress with Michael today, which makes me think I should stay away from Alex, but I can't shake the feeling that I still just wanted to see him.

On my way home, my dad calls me. "Milochka, how are you?" He doesn't wait around for me to respond, though. "Look, Natasha told me about your essay. It's no good, sweetheart. You've got to pick something else."

"What? Are you serious?" My dad has a knack for being intentionally insensitive, but this is another level right now. *He* didn't agonize over what to write. *He* didn't re-live Anya's accident in his head a million times while trying to write this essay. He doesn't have the right to veto my essay.

"The whole thing just doesn't work."

"And what would you have me write about, then?"

"Write about this challenge with Anya—it'll make people feel things, and that's always good." It sounds like he's in a marketing meeting, trying to advertise the latest technology, not helping his *daughter* with her grad school application.

"I'm not going to use Anya's misfortune to my advantage."

"That's not what I'm saying, Mila. I'm saying that what you two have gone through is a challenge, so why not write about it?" I can't help but cringe when he says 'you two'—first, because isn't Anya *his* daughter?

And second, because lately Anya and I haven't done much together, so it feels untrue to write about 'our' challenge.

I'm silent for so long that eventually he says, "Look, you don't have to write about that, but you do need to finish your application."

"I know."

"And, as an incentive for you to get them in—" He pauses for effect. "I'm cutting off the horse funding until you submit them."

It takes me a full minute to understand what he's saying, but then it hits me like Cyrus just kicked me in the chest. "Dad!"

"Mila, if this is the only way I can get you to do something..."

"I just registered for classes for this weekend at WEF—"

"The card will be declined. If you want to compete, you'll have to pay for them yourself."

"But, Cyrus, his boarding and food—"

"The boarding is paid for through the month, so as long as you get your applications in before the end of the month, Cyrus will be fine."

"And if I don't?"

"That's your choice."

I hang up on my dad—something I've *never* done—fury radiating through me. He doesn't even bother to call me back.

I know my dad can be a bully in the business world, but to bully *me* into submission is just wrong. And then I'm mad because if Anya were around, this wouldn't be happening. He wouldn't care what I was doing or not doing, because the golden child would be doing his bidding. But now here I am, essentially the *only* child, and I have to take the full brunt of my dad's motivational tactics.

I want to call someone, but who? Normally I'd call Michael, or Anya. But Michael feels completely off-limits to me right now, at least until I compete—*if* I compete. And Anya? How thoughtless of me to vent to Anya about all the things I can do in my able-bodied life, while she's stuck in bed. I think about calling Monica, but then remember that she has a night lecture she's in right now. My fingers hover over my contacts, and I'm punching in a name before I even think about it.

He picks up on the third ring. "Mila?"

"Hey, Alex," I say, suddenly feeling embarrassed I called him. I eek out, "What are you up to right now?"

I sit in my car outside my house talking to Alex for what feels like minutes, but when I get off the phone, I realize it's been over an hour. Despite everything that happened with my dad, I'm smiling as I ascend the stairs, and this time, I don't even pause outside of Anya's room.

I shower and brush my teeth, thinking about my conversation with Alex. I'm glad that he seems to be okay with us being friends. Because he *is* a really good friend. And it makes me feel at peace about still pursuing Michael even while Alex and I develop our friendship.

I'm lying in bed, not quite ready to fall asleep, scrolling through Instagram. Trina posted a picture of Cyrus and me in the High Amateur's from Sunday on the barn's IG account, so I respond to several positive comments from other riders. There's a warmth in my chest spreading through my limbs. I can do this. I can compete in the Grand Prix this Sunday, I can show Michael that I've changed, and I can win him back. I'll have to use my own money—winnings from various horse shows, particularly last weekend when I won the Low Amateur Classic. It'll all but clean out my bank account, but it's worth it.

The only thing I'm unsure about is how I'll pay for gas—because I drive, like, *a lot*. With the barn in Wellington, school in Miami, and my house in Weston, I'm guzzling gas like I'm a cross-country trucker. Maybe if I stay with Monica on the days I have school, and only go to Wellington when I absolutely need to, I can manage until I get my applications in.

I'm scrolling farther down my feed when a picture of Amber and Michael pops up. All of the warmth I'd been feeling freezes and dies within me. They're smiling, their faces pressed together as they take a selfie. I scroll through the other pictures on the post, and it turns out they went paddle boarding. She's wearing the tiniest bikini known to womankind and just that fact sends frissons of anger down my spine. At least her boobs are small, I think bitterly.

Seeing their pictures makes me think of the time Michael took me kayaking on a dolphin tour around People's Island near North Miami. The dolphins were so close to our boat that you could reach out and touch them. And of course Michael did do that—even though the tour guide told him not to—and he toppled his kayak. It took him forever to get back in his boat because every time he tried to jump back on, the kayak would flip over. I smile at the memory, before it comes crashing down and I realize Michael is making memories with some other girl. It's hard to imagine all of Michael's thoughtfulness being channeled into someone that's not me.

I sit up in bed, and my chest feels tight, like all the emotions swirling around in there are threatening to burst out. I'm angry—that Michael broke up with me, that he went out with Amber, that I have to prove myself to him to even have a chance to get him back. We dated for over two years—isn't that proof enough that I love him? And shouldn't love be enough to keep someone?

Before long, Monica's texting me about what a sheisty *pajero* Michael is, and she's attempting to cajole me into taking pics with Alex and posting them online. But I'm not willing to do that. I want Michael to want me back, not because he's jealous, but because he loves me.

Since I'm a glutton for punishment, I spend far too much time searching through the entirety of Michael and then Amber's Instagram history, and I find something interesting: a few pictures of Amber and Alex from several months ago. There's nothing about the pictures that seem romantic—at the very least Amber is *clothed* in the pictures—but it gives me pause. I didn't realize Alex and Amber were close. Seeing the two of them together makes me feel some type of way I'm not sure how to interpret. I remember Alex basically ignoring Amber's attempts to talk to him at Kickback a few weeks ago, and I wonder if it's rooted in something more. Did they date? Did she hurt him? Did he cast her aside?

After scrutinizing the captions, examining who liked the pictures, and analyzing Alex's seemingly platonic smile (or is that just my wishful thinking?), I put my phone away and attempt to watch *Heartland*. But I can't even calm down enough to pay attention, so I slip out of bed and tiptoe to Anya's room. There's no light coming from under her door, so I walk in. It takes a few seconds for my eyes to adjust to the dark, but Anya's asleep and my mom is too, in the cot next to my sister's bed. I approach the bed and kneel beside it, clasping Anya's arm, my head resting next to her shoulder. I wait for the tears to come, I wait for Anya to wake up, but it doesn't happen. Eventually, I go back to my room and fall into a fitful sleep.

# Chapter Ten

# Señorita

The next day, I use my horse show winnings to register for the Sunday Grand Prix as well as a schooling class on Saturday. I decide to sleep over Monica's during the week and then on the weekend I'll stay at Trina's so I don't waste gas. Not going to the barn during the week forces me to work on my application essay, which is utterly painful to the extreme. I write about Anya's accident. I delete it. I write about it again. I delete it again. How can I possibly let a stranger—or a whole committee of strangers—into the worst moment of my life? Why is that socially acceptable?

"What about writing something related to your horseback riding?" Monica suggests one afternoon.

"Like what?"

"Didn't you say that you're moving up in divisions, but that was hard for you, especially after Anya's accident? You could mention the accident but not have to delve into your deepest, darkest fears..."

"That's actually not a terrible idea except for the part where my trainer literally tricked me into moving up, and then I ultimately took the leap because I'm trying to win back my boyfriend."

"Well, if I were you, I'd leave that part out."

"No kidding. Hey, Stanford, want me? I'm a desperate loser who's pining over her boyfriend and can't do anything productive without being manipulated into it."

"Yeah...definitely leave that part out."

By the end of our study session, I have a pretty decent outline for my essay. I check my phone and there's a text from Michael. It's Khan with a cone on his head with the caption *Someday I'll be a unicorn.*

I laugh and show it to Monica, who chuckles, because I guess only horse people truly appreciate horse humor.

"So, you're talking again?"

I shrug. "I...guess so."

"Isn't he moving?"

"Yes, which is why I need to do this."

She shakes her head, confused and speaks slowly when she says, "So that he can miss you when he's gone...?"

I roll my eyes. "So that we can get back together before he leaves."

She mutters something under her breath in Spanish and I know it's not good.

"People date long-distance all the time. Besides, I can move. I'm planning on going to grad school."

"Are you?" She quirks an eyebrow at me.

I groan and wave a hand at her. This conversation with Monica has brought my anxiety to an all-time high. It's like trying to clamp a lid on a pot of boiling water—it's threatening to overflow, yet I can't turn down the heat. Soon it'll bubble over, and I'm not sure what will become of me when that happens.

I return to my text with Michael and send him a 'lol' in lower caps—not too desperate—and resist the urge to send him one of the hundred horse memes I have saved in a folder on my phone. Instead, I tuck my phone away and Monica and I head back to her dorm, where I eat a Cup of Noodles for dinner while we watch the latest episodes of *Down to Earth* with Zac Efron.

By the time Friday rolls around, I'm so nervous for the Grand Prix that I'm barely sleeping at night. My schooling class is 1.45m and it's a speed challenge, which means there's no jump off. It's just one round, and whoever goes fastest with the least amount of faults wins. Trina chose this class to get my feet wet. "You only have to worry about one round," she said, but the speed part is getting to my head.

Even though it's January, it's as hot as summer today and there's sweat pouring down my back as we walk the course. I already have my helmet on and I keep needing to wipe sweat from my forehead so it doesn't drip in my eyes.

Trina keeps saying, "Just take it slow, pretend it's a practice course. It *is* a practice course."

"Right," I say, not at all convinced.

I'm early in the lineup, so when we're done walking the course, Alex already has Cyrus waiting for me in the schooling ring. It's the first time I've seen him since our disastrous sort-of-date, and I'm not sure how to act. Do I hug him? Do I just wave? We talked on the phone, and that felt very comfortable, but I'm all out of sorts by the time I reach him. Thankfully, Alex only gives me a big smile, which I try to return. And I'm sure I look like a baboon attempting to smile, because that's how I feel.

I get on Cyrus and start warming him up, going over the course in my mind. Alex and Trina set up the middle jump in the practice ring and I start cantering over a small oxer. Cyrus seems surprisingly relaxed, like he's done this a million times before, and it helps me calm down. Trina continually raises the practice fence until it's at the very top of the standards, but Cyrus and I are jumping it like it's any old jump at home. There are several other horses and riders circling the schooling ring, but they all fade into the background as Cyrus and I meld over the jump.

Finally, it's our turn. We stand at the in-gate, and I can't help the flashback of Anya on the ground. I'm picturing her helmeted head crunching into the sand. The image comes and then it goes as I force myself to watch the rider on course. He's going over the triple combination and then making the rollback to the liverpool. The liverpool is a type of water jump that isn't the sprawling kind—it's more like a regular vertical with a blue tarp–like piece underneath. Anything to get the horses weirded out. *Not this horse*, I think as I pat Cyrus's neck. I'm steadier than I've ever felt with Cyrus as we trot into the ring, past the vertical water jump, and wait for the buzzer.

I feel zen, like I could teach a yoga class right about now. And then the buzzer chimes, and every ounce of calm is flung from my mind as Cyrus rockets onto the course. I barely get him under control to point him at the first jump, a black and gold CDD Wealth oxer. Before I can blink, we've flown over it and it's four hurried strides to the green Rolex vertical.

It's as if Cyrus got the memo that this was a speed class—I'm pulling at his mouth, but he is *not* slowing down. As we're going over the Rolex jump, he seems to sense that we need to turn, so he's turning mid-air, but in the wrong direction. When we land, he's going right, but we need to go left. I'm tugging on the left rein, and we end up making a very wide rollback to the liverpool. The back-and-forth slows Cyrus down, but only for a little bit. After we fly over the water jump, it's another quick rollback to the triple combination. Our rollback is so tight, it's like he's almost laying down.

We charge into the first jump of the triple, put in one stride instead of two, and I'm left behind as we go over the second jump. He clears it, despite me flapping around like a sack of potatoes on his back, and then it's another stride as we jump the last vertical in the combination. It's not very rhythmic, but we get through clear.

It's a long gallop to the next line—and Cyrus is booking it, even though I'm standing on my toes, pulling back on the reins. I'm so frantic I can barely catch my breath. As we approach the first jump in the line, I'm overwhelmed by how impenetrable it is—it's a bright white wall, solid from the ground to the top, and it seems to be emanating difficulty. And Cyrus is blitzing toward it like it's the enemy.

It seems as though he's going to leave long, but at the last second he adds in a quick stride. He has to make a humongous effort to get over it from that angle, and I'm tossed up with him, only hanging on by my stirrups. I feel his front legs graze the top of the jump, and the topmost bricks fall to the ground as we land.

We were planning to go on the outside path for this broken line, but Cyrus has a different idea. He's going inside, and he's going in six strides instead of seven. Again, we land and I'm practically falling on his neck. Cyrus is anticipating the turn, and this time he guesses right. We go inside the butterfly jump to a skinny plank and finally we have a jump where I'm acting like a decent rider. I'm actually in the saddle, giving him a good release, and landing without scrambling myself back together.

I try to catch my breath—and fail—as we ride toward the in-and-out. "Whoa," I call to Cyrus. His ears twitch back at the sound of my voice, and he actually listens this time. He slows his pace just a hair, and we find a perfect distance to the two-jump combo. In, then, out.

One final gallop to the last jump—the spectacularly gaudy WEF jump, with horses jumping from the side of the standards and every flag of every country competing at WEF represented on the poles. We're thundering toward it, Cyrus's hooves hitting the arena floor, the sound jolting through my chest into my heart. Right before we get to the jump, I sit back, adjust Cyrus, and we soar over it. Then, we're racing through the timers, and I hear Trina and Alex cheering at the in-gate.

It wasn't pretty, but we did it. I slow Cyrus and throw my arms around his neck. "Good boy," I tell him, "Good, good boy."

As I'm untacking Cyrus, I get a text from Monica: *Where we partying tonight??* along with a GIF of Leslie Knope dancing like a goof. As if Monica has ever looked so nerdy.

Me: ... *Wellington?*

Monica: *Laaaaame.*

Monica: *Send me an address.*

Monica: *This is me showing you how much I love your melancholy self. Choosing Welly-world over MIAMI.*

Me: *You love me.*

Monica: *Uh huh.*

I smile as I shake my head at my phone.

"What are you smiling about over there?" Alex asks. "I mean, aside from the fact that you went in the International Arena—by choice this time—and you're still alive."

"Yes, that is definitely something to be smiling about," I tell him, trying not to dwell on the fact that this guy seems to know me *so* well. "It's my friend, Monica. She's coming up here tonight."

"Where are you going to go?"

"Dunno, I guess wherever everyone else is going."

Turns out a few people were already planning to go to Clematis Social, so I head to Trina's to shower and change. Monica meets me there, and she gives me a look when I come out in my jeans and tank top.

"You're *not* going out in that."

"It's the only thing I brought."

She sighs deeply, like I'm the biggest inconvenience of her life, and says, "It's a good thing I'm such a good friend," and she rummages into her purse and pulls out a shirt for me. Except, come to find out, it's not a shirt. It's a dress the size of a shirt.

"Oh Mi-ami," Monica says when I come back out.

"I can't wear this. It barely covers my butt."

"Mila, Mila, Mila." She's shaking her head at me. "That's how it's supposed to look. Like, when they made this dress, this is exactly what they had in mind. Mila Kozak, precisely like that." She waves a finger at me. "*Es perfecto.*"

I roll my eyes, but I'm not ready to lose this battle. "Monica, look at my legs. They're so white. This is why I wear jeans." (Aside from the fact that they *cover more than just my butt.*) "Horse people problems. We always have super tanned upper bodies but our legs are pasty as Casper the ghost, and let me tell you, it's not so friendly."

Monica's laughing, but not in a defeated kind of way. She simply thrusts a hand back into her purse—which is apparently some kind of Mary Poppins-esque bag—and pulls out a bottle, tossing it to me.

Self-tanner. I groan.

Twenty minutes later, I'm in Monica's car in her microscopic dress, with three coats of tanning gel on my legs. "I hope you're happy," I grumble.

"You are my joy, *princesa.*"

"What would you do without me?"

"Find some other horse girl to play dress up with, probably. Maybe...that Amber girl?"

I slice my eyes at her and she's laughing. "Too soon?"

I shake my head, there are no words to express how I feel about the Amber situation.

"She's got nothing on you, Mila."

"Thanks," I mumble.

"I'm serious. Chin up, you are on fire tonight."

A few minutes later, we pull up to Clematis. Half the barn is already there so we head to the back where the ping pong tables are. I'm a crap ping pong player—honestly anything that isn't horseback riding, I'm crap at—but Monica and I team up against Colleen and Ryan and only beat them because Monica is a beast tennis player.

After another round of ping pong, Michael struts in. He gives me an appreciative head–to–toe look and I'm glad at least he's not immune to me. A tiny spring of hope wells in me, and I wonder if my plan is going to work. If it's currently working.

I look over at Amber at the pool table, and she's pouting. But the moment Michael walks up to her to say hi, she plasters on a huge, fake smile. I groan inwardly and lean on Monica, happy she's there with me.

We order some drinks and appetizers and all play a round of pool. Clematis is starting to fill up, the DJ building steam as the music gets louder.

I'm standing next to the pool table, dipping my curly fries in ketchup when Alex walks in. I drop my fries and brush off my hands because for whatever reason tonight I don't want to be the indelicate girl shoving food in my mouth. I feel his eyes on me from all the way across the room, and it's like he's a heat-seeking missile, coming straight for me because Monica was right. I am on fire.

Alex's eyes never leave mine the entire time until he's right in front of me. And my stomach is in knots wondering what he's going to do once he gets to me. Finally, he's there, and he wraps an arm around my back, pressing me into a small hug as he kisses my cheek Spanish-style.

"Hi," he says.

"Hi," I say a little too breathlessly. Because, seriously, where did all the oxygen in the room go?

Then he lets go of me, and I can still feel where his hand was because my skin is burning like his hand is molten lava. He greets the rest of the barn crew, and Ryan says something to him that makes Alex laugh, and I have to force myself to look away because watching him is making me feel all sorts of things I shouldn't be feeling.

Monica, of course, is observing all of this with a knowing eye. She waggles her eyebrows at me and I laugh weakly, shaking my head.

We all settle on some chairs and drink our drinks, but it's too loud at this point for conversation. Monica shouts something to Ryan, who's sitting beside her, and the two of them go off dancing. Not long after, Amber and Michael and a few others join them, leaving Alex and me to hold down our seats. I sip my super girly drink that Monica ordered me—"you need to loosen up!" she shouted when she handed it to me—and tap my foot in time with the beat. Alex is sitting across from me. And he's reading a book.

I repeat, *he is reading a book.*

I squint to read the cover: *Man's Search for Meaning* by Viktor E. Frankl. And I'm just wondering about the endless depths of this guy, to be reading a book like that in the middle of all this chaos. Knowing what he told me before about coping after his dad's death, I definitely don't take it as rude, but I do think it's funny. I mean, the bass is so powerful I think it's going to rip a hole in my eardrums, and he's reading a freaking book. And not just any book, but *that* book, which I know is written by a Holocaust survivor.

It's far too loud in here for me to give him a hard time about it from all the way over here, so instead, I text him: *I can't believe you can read a book in here.*

I watch as he gets his phone out, reads my text, and then his fingers dart across his screen, typing a response. He hits send, puts his phone down, and looks me dead in the eye. His gaze is pinning me down to my seat. I can't move, and I find I don't want to.

After several long seconds, I glance down at my phone to see what he said.

Alex: *I can be very focused when I want something.*

Between the look he's giving me, the text he sent, and everything else he's said and done in the last few weeks, there are serious fireworks going off all through my body. As in, Fourth of July fireworks plus Chinese New Year and maybe add in a little Diwali, and you're getting close to what I'm experiencing.

My mind is racing and I'm trying—and epically failing—not to imagine what it would be like if Alex kissed me. And kissed me because he wanted to, not because he had to. The way he's looking at me, it's like he can read my mind, because he's wearing that super sexy half-smile that makes my knees feel a little weak.

And, oh Mi-ami, he just put his book down and he's coming over to me. He puts his hand out, and I take it, and he leads me out onto the dance floor. I notice that he intentionally leads me away from where Monica, Michael, and the other barn people are all dancing.

Right as we hit the dance floor, the DJ starts playing Camila Cabello and Shawn Mendes's "Senorita." And, let me just say, *wow.* Alex is a phenomenal dancer. Sure, we slow-danced at Maxwell's Plum last week, but that was just swaying. This is actual dancing, and I am nowhere near up to speed. But he seems to know how to direct me with little touches of his hand, and slowly everything around us starts to fall away until I'm certain we're the only ones left on the dance floor.

Every time he spins me, I feel a temporary shock at being separated from him, and when he pulls me back, it's like coming home. When Camila sings about being more than just friends, Alex locks eyes with me and I melt. I'm sure if his hands weren't there holding me together, I would be a puddle at his feet.

The song ends way too soon, and then we're dancing to Calvin Harris's "Feels." I'm wishing Alex would take a cue from Pharrell and steal a kiss from me when suddenly Trina is there, clearly looking for the rest of our friends. There's physical pain when I peel my eyes away from Alex's as we lead Trina over to where they're all dancing. I do my best to dance with the rest of the crew when really all I want to do is go back to Alex's arms.

And then there they are, Alex and Michael, both inhabiting the same space, and I am utterly torn. I can't pretend I don't have some sort of feelings for Alex, but I also can't deny the years I've invested with Michael.

At some point during a David Guetta/Bebe Rexha song, Alex disappears. I want to follow him, but I also know that Monica drove all this way up here for me. So I dance until I'm certain my feet will fall off, but that discomfort is nowhere near the wrenching in my stomach from the anarchy going on in there. I'm thinking over this whole situation with Alex—why did I need to kiss him? Why did I need to open that door and let this chaos out? Forget Pandora's box, I just smashed through the gate of her whole galaxy.

When I head to the bathroom, Amber follows me, and she is sloppy drunk. The girl can barely walk in controlled zig-zag, much less a straight line. After, when we're washing our hands, Amber says, "Me and Michael have been hanging out" as if I needed her to point that out to me.

"Cool," I say as casually as I can, even though there's low-key rage simmering in my chest. And it comes back to me that there's also the question mark of her relationship with Alex, and I'm wondering what is *with* this girl and why is she all up in my space.

"So you're down with it?" she says as she kind of throws herself at me in a weird attempt at a hug. "You are *so* nice, Mila."

"No one's ever accused me of that, Amber," I grumble as we walk out of the bathroom.

When we get back on the dance floor, I expect Michael to take Amber's hand since they've been dancing together a good chunk of the night, but instead he comes up to me and leans in, his mouth so close to my ear that his lips brush against my skin as he talks. "How about one dance? For old times?"

And while it doesn't feel as electric as my dance with Alex, dancing with Michael feels safe and comfortable. I know how his body moves, and he knows me. We fall into a familiar rhythm and there's something really comforting about that. And I'm just left wondering why he'd give that up. Dancing with him breaks open a part of me that I thought was healing, but instead it feels like a scab I just scraped off. I'm bleeding all over again, while also wishing Alex were here to staunch the bleeding and I just don't know if that's fair to him at all.

Then, I look over and see Amber's face—and let me just say, she is *pissed*. And right now, I feel like that moment is worth at least some amount of heartbreak on my part.

# Chapter Eleven

# Midnight Snack

That night, I dream I'm on course in the International Arena with Cyrus, except I don't know the course. Trina's at the in-gate, yelling out to me where to go, but I can't hear her. We're galloping around the ring, looking at the jump numbers, but none of them are in order and the numbers don't make sense. An impossibly high fan jump is number 113 and then there's a water jump that looks like the Everglades—complete with swampy reeds and a handful of alligators floating on top. Cyrus is charging the water and I'm pulling at his mouth like my life depends on it. But he's not listening.

We fly over the water, and for a second I think we're going to make it, and then Cyrus starts to fall. We plummet into the swamp and I'm tossed away from Cy. I'm grasping for him, for something, anything, to hold on to. But it's just water all around me. I look up and realize I'm miles below the surface. I start swimming furiously, my limbs and chest burning with the exertion, and then the alligators close in. They're snapping and whipping their tails around like I'm they're next meal.

The biggest one—a green-gray beast that looks like he missed the memo that the Jurassic period ended—is hurtling toward me. I'm searching for Cyrus, but he's not there. I'm swimming away, but suddenly my legs aren't working. Then my arms aren't either. I'm paralyzed. Just floating in the water, waiting for the alligator to get me. His jaws open, those menacing teeth glistening in the water. His mouth closes around my head, and I jolt awake, panting.

And suddenly, my chest is feeling tight, like I can't catch my breath, and my heart is beating way too fast. I curl forward onto Trina's couch and I'm trying to do *anything* that will make this feeling go away. I count backward from one hundred. I look through my horse memes folder. I do jumping jacks.

I curl back up on the couch, hyperventilating, when Trina bursts into the living room.

"Let's get out of here, chica," she says, hands on her hips, as she examines me. "It's not good to lay around all day worrying. Isn't that in the Bible somewhere?" And with that, she rips the covers off of me.

I groan, but inwardly I'm glad she's coaxing me out of my panic attack. As I brush my teeth and get dressed, I'm thinking about last night, examining every minute detail about my dance with Alex, and then with Michael. In part to keep myself from having a meltdown, but also because I can't help it. Last night was...interesting. I'd be lying if I said there wasn't *something* there with Alex, but how to define it? I'm not sure.

Not for the first time, I wish I had Anya to help me sort out my feelings. She'd have a pithy question that would clarify everything, or some insight that I wouldn't have considered on my own.

I feel sad because I know our distance is my own fault, but I don't know how to breach that barrier now that it's there. Maybe Michael's right and I do need counseling. It helped Alex, didn't it? But even taking that step feels like an insurmountable difficulty.

I spend the day running around the showgrounds, helping Trina's other riders—I set practice jumps, flat and school horses, and lend a supportive cheer as I watch my friends and barn mates compete.

At the end of the day, I'm utterly exhausted but somehow I'm tossing and turning on Trina's couch, knowing I desperately need to sleep for my Grand Prix tomorrow, while also being fully convinced that there's no chance I'll fall asleep right now. Crazy thoughts ping-pong through my head—from Cyrus flipping over a jump and killing me to us winning the whole shebang. I see my neck breaking a hundred times, and also see us taking a victory lap around the International Arena. The whole thing is oppressive, and finally I'm driven to my phone for distraction. I scroll through Insta, then Pinterest, skip around on my library app looking for a new book. Eventually I relent and, because obviously I'm a glutton for punishment, I text Alex: *Can't sleep.*

Alex: *what else is new?*

Me: *ha.*

Alex: *sorry. Not surprised though, don't you normally have a hard time sleeping? Much less before your first ever GP?*

Me: *thanks for raising my expectations.*

Alex: *it's what I do.*

Me: *don't you have some good therapy techniques?*

Alex: *I think you're confused. I WENT to a therapist, I am not a therapist.*

Me: *ooooooohhhhhh*

Alex: *I know, it's confusing*

Me: *ok but seriously, no tips?*

Alex: *have you done the 4-7-8 breathing thing?*

Me: *not yet. I'll try that.*

Alex: *I'll be here. Lmk if that works.*

I lay back down on the couch and take several sets of 4-7-8 breaths—in for four seconds, hold for seven, out for eight. It does calm me down, but definitely doesn't get me any closer to sleep. Also, I can't help but think about Alex saying, 'I'll be here.' It's a simple phrase, but why does it make me feel all melty inside?

Me: *I'm not asleep yet*

Alex: *it's only been 3 minutes*

Me: *I think I just don't want to sleep*

Alex: *what do you want to do?*

I lay back, considering my response as my heart beats way faster than it has any business doing. The first thought that pops into my mind is 'talk with you' but that would take things to a more serious level way too fast.

Or, would it?

Me: *I kind of like what I'm doing right now.*

Alex: *which is....?*

Me: *talking to you dummy*

Alex takes a while to respond. I can tell he types out a few options and deletes them before sending a smiley face. I don't know what else to say, but I clutch my phone to my chest, smiling like an idiot for a few long seconds. When my phone vibrates again, I quickly unlock it as if I'm going to somehow miss the text if I don't look fast enough.

Alex: *ok, so the experts say that if you're not falling asleep, you should get out of bed and do something calming before trying again to go to sleep.*

Me: *calming. Calming. I'm not sure I know how to do anything calming except ride a horse.*

Alex: *hate to break it to you, Mila, but I don't think jumping a fifteen hundred pound animal over obstacles that are taller than you counts as 'calming'*

Me: *lolololol you have a point there*

Me: *so...what do you do when you need to calm?*

Alex: *honestly, I like going downstairs and just sitting in the barn. That calms me. The nighttime sounds of the horses, the smell of the hay. I guess it feels safe to me.*

Me: *I like that.*

Alex: *you're at Trina's, right?*

Me: *yeah*

Alex: *the barn's not that far...*

Me: *yeah...*

Alex: *I'll pick you up in 5*

Me: *no, Alex, really that's ok. You should be asleep.*

Alex: *yeah, but I'm not. I want to help you. I'm a therapist, remember? ;) see you in 5*

I unravel myself from the blanket on the couch and tiptoe over to the door and slide into my shoes. I glance down at myself—I'm wearing my pajamas, which aren't so much pajamas as an oversized t-shirt and threadbare shorts. I pull them down as far as they'll go and then slowly open the door of Trina's apartment.

It takes me a minute to get down the stairs and into the parking lot, and the whole time my heart is pounding like I'm doing something illegal. I'm just hanging out with Alex, I tell myself. We are just friends.

Friends hanging out in the middle of the night.

But when his car pulls into the parking lot and he gets out of the driver's side door, the feeling swirling in my abdomen doesn't exactly feel *friendly*. And when he approaches me and wraps an arm around me in a quick hug, my heart jumps into my throat and my whole body feels like it's on fire even though it's chilly out.

"Ready, madam, for your calming evening barn tour?" he says in a very bad British accent as he opens the passenger door with a flourish. I giggle like I'm thirteen freaking years old and hop into the car. Alex jogs around the bumper and slides into his seat before pulling out his phone and turning on music.

"Julia Michaels?" I say as I hear the first few chords of "What a Time."

"Calming enough for you?"

I nod, smiling up at him, and oh my gosh the look that he's giving me in return is very much the opposite of how a friend would look at another friend. We're frozen in this gaze, and I'm so sure he's about to kiss me when he puts the car in reverse and pulls out of the parking lot.

He rolls the windows down and turns the music up and I close my eyes, letting the breeze whip my hair all around my face. Alex's hand is on the gear shifter, which is right next to my leg, and I can feel the heat emanating from him. What if I took his hand? And then I'm thinking about how his hand might feel on my leg, the roughness on my smooth skin. I open my eyes and shake my head; I really can't let myself go down this path. Alex is my friend. I'm only thinking about these things because I kissed him to help him. And that was the right thing to do, but my feelings need to get themselves in check because I couldn't forgive myself if I hurt Alex.

I take a deep breath and gather up my hair into a hair tie. Now that my eyes are open, I can tell that Alex is glancing at me every few seconds.

I don't have the guts to meet his gaze. Not after the thoughts I was having about him.

We finally arrive at the barn, and I fling myself out of the car before we're all the way stopped. So much for *calming*.

But the moment I step into the tranquil darkness of the barn, I do feel more at peace. There are fewer horses here because most of them are at WEF, but there are still all the sounds of a barn—stomping, snorting, tail swishing. And I wonder why no one has added 'barn sounds' to a white noise app. I could fall asleep to this every night.

Missy, whose stall is facing the parking area, sticks her head over her stall door, ears perked at us. I walk to her and pet her soft nose. I read this article one time that said petting a dog for ten minutes increases your endorphin levels, and I'm certain that petting a horse for five seconds does the same. At least it does for me.

Alex walks over and Missy turns her head to snuffle at his shirt. Alex pulls a mint out of his pocket and hands it to Missy, who gobbles it.

"Is that how you get all the horses to love you? You bribe them?" I cross my arms and lean against the barn wall, looking at Alex. I realize he's wearing plaid pajama pants and an old Tryon shirt. I wouldn't have pictured Alex as a pajama pants kind of guy, but he nonetheless looks good. Even in pajama pants.

"Here I thought it was my charming personality," he says with his glorious smile, and my stomach turns like it's a flipping gymnast.

*Crap.*

Crap. Crap. Crap.

"You should wear those shorts more often," Alex says, glancing down at my legs.

I laugh, but feel warmth in my cheeks as I say, "Can't exactly ride in shorts."

"More's the pity."

I'm seriously one second away from checking my temperature—I feel so warm, I must be coming down with a fever. It's the only reasonable explanation as to why I'm feeling this way.

Alex and I walk around the barn slowly, our arms occasionally brushing against each other, sparks skittering down my arm every time.

"Oh, I have something for you," he says. "I'll be right back."

He disappears to his upstairs apartment, and I'm telling myself I need to get a grip. I take a few deep breaths, pulling my hair off of my neck to try to cool down. I'm committed to being absolutely chaste with Alex when he returns carrying a cup and a bowl.

"Midnight snack?" I say, an eyebrow raised.

"Something like that. I looked up some foods that are supposed to help you sleep." He hands me the bowl and it's got yogurt, nuts, and berries on top. "The yogurt and almonds are supposed to help you sleep, and then the blueberry smoothie has spinach and avocado in it which is high in magnesium which promotes sleep. Besides, you hardly eat when you compete so I figured it couldn't hurt to get some extra calories in now."

"Wow," I say, and all my resolve is melting away. Thankfully my hands are full with Alex's offerings, so I don't do anything except walk to the nearest tack trunk and take a seat so I can start eating. Alex sits beside me, and our legs aren't quite touching, but the space between us may as well be an electromagnetic current.

"You should be a therapist," I say between bites.

He chuckles and leans his head back against the barn wall, his eyes closed. I realize then how tired he is—he's not used to staying up so late like I am—and yet he's here. For me. And as good as that makes me feel, it also makes me feel horrible.

The horse beside us, a roan gelding aptly named Rowan, extends his nose toward us, sniffing. Without opening his eyes, Alex grabs a mint from his pocket and hands it to Rowan.

"Do you have a never ending supply of mints in your pockets? Is it like one of those clown car tricks?"

Alex laughs.

"Are you a magician?" I whisper—a little deliriously—over my yogurt bowl.

"I thought I was a therapist."

"A therapist–magician."

"Good combo."

"Agreed."

I smile and return to my parfait as Rowan lengthens the top of his nose to ruffle Alex's hair.

"Hey, can I ask you something?"

"Sure."

"How close are you and Amber?"

He peeks at me through half-closed eyes and asks, "Why?"

*Why* is a very good question, and one that I'm not sure I can answer. I shouldn't care about how close Amber and Alex are or were, but I do. I find that I care a lot. And it's not because of Amber.

"I just saw some pictures of you guys on Instagram, and I just wondered."

"Spying on me, Mila Kozak?"

"You're not on Instagram, so *no* I wasn't spying." *On you,* I should say. "I was randomly scrolling through her Insta the other day and saw pics of you guys."

"We hung out a few times a couple months ago. It was casual."

I have so many questions, but I don't know how to ask them without sounding like I care more than I do. Does 'hanging out' to Alex mean something like *this*? Am I *hanging out* with Alex right now? Did he do this with Amber, too? And, more importantly, why is this so unsettling to me? I think about Amber's comment at Clematis and I wonder if she's with Michael right now. My brain is telling me that that should bother me more right now, but my body is telling me something else. Something else having to do with Alex being so close to me.

I'm silent for a while, and for a second I think maybe Alex has fallen asleep, but then he says, "If I don't have feelings for someone, and they do, I'm not one to string them along."

The words hit like daggers. Is he accusing me of something? Right now I wish I could deny my feelings for Alex, but I can't. However, I also can't pretend I'm not trying to get back with Michael. Because I am. The whole thing makes me feel like garbage, and I'm about to put my food down and get out of here when Alex says, "Have you thought any more about what you want to do?" And I think he's talking about what I want to do with him, or Michael.

I stare at him for a long time before I respond. "Uh, with what?"

"Life after college? Still going through with the applications?"

I breathe a sigh of relief; he's not asking about my feelings for him. But it's a precarious relief—I know I'm not going to get away with this forever. Alex is too perceptive for that. "Seeing as my dad has Cyrus and me by the balls, yeah."

"You don't have to be beholden to him, you know."

I think about this for a minute. Is that true? Do I *want* to go against my dad's wishes? I know that I could get a job, and work every second of every day to pay for Cyrus's room and board. A cheap sport this is not. But I could do it.

"Can I tell you something?" I finally say, and despite all of my conflicting feelings and guilt, I still want to spill my guts to Alex. He feels safer than anyone I've interacted with for a long time.

"Of course."

"I used to think...before Anya, y'know, I used to think that I wanted to ride professionally. Compete in Grand Prixs, teach, maybe even own a barn one day. I'd have a full suite of Grand Prix horses to choose from, competing with multiple horses in each show. Teaching on the side, not because I need to but because I want to."

"And now?"

"Now..." I trail off, trying to find the right words, but nothing truly apt comes up. I settle on, "I'm scared," but that doesn't even begin to cover it.

"But you're competing tomorrow...maybe you're scared but at least you're facing your fear."

"Yes, but what if I compete tomorrow and it doesn't measure up to what was in my head? Or, what if I'm just not that same girl anymore? You said before that grief fundamentally changes who you are. Is this new Mila temporary, or is she forever? It feels like one way or another that's going to get answered tomorrow."

"Hmm," Alex says, which is usually my line.

"Did my mumbo-jumbo of feelings actually rupture the therapist hiding in there?" I ask, playfully tapping his temple. He turns to look at me, his tired eyes so dark and serious, that it gives me pause.

"Mila?"

"Yeah?"

"I don't want to be your therapist." His words are almost a whisper.

"What do you want?" I ask, the words rasping my throat.

"I would've thought that's pretty clear," he says with a twist of his full lips. And then his eyes are devouring me, like he can see into me and wants every piece of me. It's an overwhelming feeling—one I adore and dread at the same time. After a few seconds, I look away. Alex sighs, and that sigh just rips through me, like it's an indictment on what a terrible person I am for torturing Alex. For torturing myself, too. He turns away from me, returning to his previous head tilt, eyes closed. "I think that what you're feeling is very understandable. The reality is that no one knows what tomorrow will bring, and we'll just have to face it, whatever happens."

"We?"

He cracks his eyes open and slants them at me. "Yes, we." He takes my hand, and I let him. He squeezes it as if to confirm what he just said, and then he fans my fingers out on his leg, just above his knee, and starts running a finger up and down each of my fingers, and who in the world knew something so simple could feel so good? With each stroke, it feels like a million pinpricks of light are erupting under his fingers. And then I'm aware of his very defined muscle under my palm, and my breath hitches in my throat.

And then I'm chastising myself because what in the name of Gem Twist is happening? I'm a 21-year-old woman who is freaking out because another adult is touching my hand. I'm trying to convince myself that this is normal—something that *friends* do. I know I'm kidding myself, but the truth seems too hard to accept right now.

Then Alex is saying something, and it takes all of my mental energy to focus on the words coming out of his mouth instead of what his fingers are doing as they skate across my skin.

"I do know that trauma, grief, it does change you. But I also know it gets easier, especially if you do what you need to do to heal. Maybe you'll never be the old Mila again, but in the end, you could be a better Mila."

"Hmm." I set down my empty parfait bowl and then take a sip of the blueberry smoothie. It's thick and creamy, probably because of the avocado. I'm reflecting on what he said. Will I really never be back to the old Mila? As much as I don't want that to be true—as much as my plan to win Michael back hangs on that—what he's saying seems accurate. Maybe I can't be old Mila, but I can work toward a new Mila that I'm happy with.

*Right?*

I bring my legs up to my chest, careful not to upset my hand still on Alex's leg, while I finish my smoothie. I'll definitely give Alex credit because I feel a lot calmer *and* I also think the whole eating-in-the-middle-of-the-night thing is going to pay off tomorrow when I know I won't feel like eating.

I set the cup down and soon find myself drifting, my head falling to one side and jerking back up. Alex's movements over my hand have slowed down, too. And before I know it, there's light streaming through the barn breezeway. I peel my eyes open, squinting into the daylight, and I realize I'm practically draped across Alex. My head is in the crook of his neck and my legs, which I had tucked up to my chest during the night, have fallen over his legs. His arm is around my back, gently holding me to him even as he sleeps. I peek at his face, his eyes still closed, his breathing light and steady. He's so at peace, and somehow he seems very vulnerable, too. Before I even realize what I'm doing, I reach up and kiss him on the cheek. He's asleep, I reason, he'll never know. But the second my lips press against his stubbled cheek, his eyes flutter open. Like me, it takes him a moment to realize what happened. And then he gives me a bashful—and very adorable—look out of the corner of his eye, his smile spreading across his face.

His hand lingers on my waist, and he sort of squeezes me to him for a second before releasing me. "I, uh, thought you were going to fall over last night," he says, explaining why his arm was wrapped around me, and I wonder if he even needs to give a reason. He rubs his hands across his face. "I'm sorry, I should've taken you home earlier. I tried to wake you a few times, but you were out." He laughs to himself. "As in, I checked your breathing a few times."

"I guess that spinach worked," I laugh. "Honestly, any sleep last night is a win for me."

"That's kind of what I thought, too," he says as he reaches over and tucks a strand of hair behind my ear. I've always read about guys doing that in novels, but I never realized any of them did it in real life. And, let me tell you, it's a little magical as his fingertips linger on the part of my neck right below my ear. For a second I think that he's finally going to kiss me, and I'm finally going to let him.

That is, until I see a figure walk into the breezeway. And, of course, it's none other than Michael. He's stalking into the barn like he's on a mission, but when he sees us and comes to a sudden stop.

I can't help it—I sit up and away from Alex as Michael's eyes connect with mine, and a flash of something like fury darts across his face and my insides are thrown into utter confusion. Is he jealous because I'm hanging out with Alex? Does he have a right to be? Does that mean he wants me back? My mind is going a million miles a minute and I'm completely frozen with indecision.

"Hey, uh, shouldn't you guys be at the showgrounds?" he says, looking between Alex and me.

"I, um..." can't think of anything to say that doesn't sound remotely condemning.

"She couldn't sleep last night, so she came to the barn and fell asleep on the tack trunk," Alex says, and a massive wave of shame engulfs me because Alex just stood up for me, discreetly, with my ex-boyfriend. But, why?

"I see," Michael says, but his face certainly doesn't give any indication he believes Alex's shortened version of the night. "Well, I'm just switching out my bit. I'll see you tonight, Mila?"

I feel Alex's stare, and I can't meet his gaze. Because right now, I feel like the worst person in the world. As in, there's Stalin and Hitler, then a big, shiny picture of Mila Kozak because Alex is the best guy *ever* and I'm screwing with his heart.

"Yep," I say feebly.

"Looking forward to it." Michael gives his million dollar smile—which actually cost his dad a cool ten Gs, but it's still sexy nonetheless—and then strides off to the tack room.

The tension between Alex and me suddenly flips on its head, and all the comfortable electricity we were feeling is replaced by an awkward politeness.

"Thanks for, um, everything," I say, not quite looking him in the eye.

"Happy to help, boss."

I wince at his word choice, and I'm pretty sure he notices, though he doesn't say anything. We both get up and start to walk in different directions, but then we turn around at the same time as realization dawns.

"You're my ride—"

"I brought you—"

"Right," Alex says, fishing his keys out of his pocket. "Let's get you to Trina's."

I nod and follow him to his car. We ride in silence all the way to Trina's, Alex's stony face staring straight ahead the entire way. And I wonder if it wouldn't be the worst thing in the world if Cyrus threw me six feet under in the ring today, because then at least I wouldn't have to deal with the thorny awkwardness coming from the men who were both tugging at my heart.

I walked the course twice, once with Trina and again right after on my own, and then watched the first five riders. Now I'm pacing the schooling ring, waiting for Alex to bring up Cyrus, feeling like I might just throw up every ounce of smoothie and parfait left in my system. I press a hand onto my roiling stomach, which helpfully somersaults as Alex and Cyrus walk into the ring.

When they reach me, I pivot on my heel, kneel over the fence, and heave bile out onto the walking path. Just when I think it's over, another wave hurls through me. Alex is crouching next to me, rubbing my back and murmuring something to me I can't quite hear through the retching. When it's finally done, I rest my head on my knees and try to breathe.

"Here," Alex says, holding out a bottle of water. I take it gratefully and swish the water around in my mouth and spit it out a few times before taking a couple tentative sips. Eventually Alex helps me to my feet, and I sway a bit, and of course he's there to steady me. Because after everything I've done, he's still Alex. "Well, now that that's done, I think that means you're ready."

I groan and lean my helmeted head onto his chest. Alex takes the water bottle, pours some water on his hand and then rubs it across my neck, which feels really good since I'm hot and sticky from throwing up so much.

"Mila?"

"Uh huh?"

"I know you feel like crap right now, but think about how epic this will all be once you win this thing. Or at least get around the course in one piece. It'll be a story you'll tell your kids and grandkids till they're bleeding from their ears."

I snort, which I immediately regret, because it hurt my throat, which will probably take a week to recover from the bile that burned it.

"That's your pep talk?" I gaze up at him, and his image is blurring a little.

"I thought it was pretty good."

"Maybe don't go into sports psychology."

"I'll keep that in mind," he says as he situates me next to Cyrus's saddle. Next thing I know, I'm on top of Cy and we're walking around the schooling ring while Alex and Trina are setting up a practice jump for us. I take a few deep breaths, attempting to gather all of the courage I can possibly muster—which, I'll admit, is not a ton. But it *is* enough to get me to press Cyrus into a trot, and then a canter, and then we're over the first practice jump, and the second. The movement between Cyrus and me becomes rote—something we've done a thousand times, something my muscles remember to do without me telling them to. The practice jump goes up, up, up, and then we're rolling back to it, and I can't tell where my legs end and Cyrus's body begins. Sometimes I wonder how I went so long without knowing Cyrus or having him in my life, because now he feels like an extension of myself. An appendage I didn't know was missing.

Then we're on deck, watching the rider in front of me. I'm counting their strides between jump three and four when the colossal bay horse trips and the rider goes flying headfirst into the ground. And just like that, I'm reliving Anya's accident all over again. The gelding goes galloping off, the stirrups and reins flapping in the wind as paramedics run to the center of the ring with a backboard. I can't help it, I'm shaking as if an earthquake is ripping through my core. I lean over Cyrus's shoulder and I'm gagging again, but there's nothing left to come out. Alex is at one leg, gripping my thigh, and Trina's at the other, squeezing my boot. No one says anything. The whole arena is silent, because what is there to say?

An ambulance squeals into a side entrance of the ring. The doors fly open and the motionless rider is carried into the back. As quickly as it came, it's gone.

In my whole competitive rider's life, I've seen an ambulance in the ring exactly two times: when Anya had her accident, and just now. I've taken enough statistics to know that the odds of *me* ending up on a stretcher today are low—but that doesn't stop the fear from taking my stomach into its vice grip.

One of the WEF workers is smoothing the ground where the rider fell, and I wonder, did they do that with Anya? Just clear any evidence of her eternal punishment by grating a freaking rake over the ground? The announcer is saying something about 'thoughts and prayers' and Trina's turning to me, asking me if I'm ready to go in.

"You don't have to," she says. But I know the truth—if I don't go now, I never, ever will.

"Can I just have some water?"

Alex hands me the bottle, and I take a sip. I give him back the bottle and his fingers brush over mine, giving them a squeeze. It hits me, then, how incredible Alex is. I mean, I already knew that, but how incredible he is *for me*. The look in his eyes tells me that he believes in me, even more than I do, and that belief is enough to propel me into the arena.

But first, because I'm not sure I'll make it out of the arena in one piece, I lean down toward him, grabbing his shirt in my hand and pull him into a kiss. He's startled—of course he is—and I wonder if we'll ever have a kiss where I'm not pulling a fast one on him. But he quickly sinks into it, and for a moment I'm happy because even if things go sideways in the Arena, Alex will have one last positive memory with me.

And then, just like that, I'm pushing my heels into Cyrus's side and we're cantering into the ring. I give him a good look at the liverpool, sponsored by Nutrena with its bright green standards.

"We have Miss Mila Kozak riding Cyrus Van Der Bergh of Miami, Florida on course." There's that snobby British announcer, but at least he pronounces my name correctly. You gotta cherish the little things, especially when you're about to die.

The buzzer sounds and Cyrus takes off, doing his buck-kick with his hind legs. I gather my reins, perch in the saddle and steer us to the first fence, the WEF jump with all of its multicolored flags. Before my heart even takes a beat, we're over that jump and it's a long nine strides to the next oxer. My heart is in my throat and my breathing is ragged as the wind whips through the ring.

Cyrus snorts and I feel the excitement shivering through his muscles as we charge toward the next fence. It's an airy skinny, so I sit back and pull him together before we rocket over it.

We're rollbacking to the triple combination, flying through, when Cyrus trips. He catches himself, but we've lost a lot of momentum before the most athletically challenging part of the course. I dig my heels in and click my tongue at him.

"C'mon, Cy," I encourage him as we're only two strides out from the triple. He picks up some speed, but it's not enough to get through it smoothly. We chip in, adding another stride before we launch into the combination. He does his best to arch over the first, then the second, but on the third, it's just too much for him and we knock the rail down. But we get through.

The next obstacle is an option—we can make a tight turn to a brick vertical or a wider turn to a massive oxer. I was originally planning to go with the vertical, but we need to regain some speed, so I take the outside option and squeeze my legs around Cyrus to really get him moving.

We soar over the oxer and we're in freefall for a second, until we jolt to the ground and it's a long, broken line to the next jump. I lose count of the strides, and before I know it we're leaving long. I get caught behind and end up accidentally jerking at Cyrus's mouth. He takes it in stride, though, like the gem that he is, and by the time we get to the in–and–out we're back in rhythm. We find the perfect distance and it's in, then out, as we fly through the combination. I steer him over the liverpool oxer, which he gives a wide berth over, and then we're shooting through the last line, flying toward the final jump, a very knock-downable vertical.

"Whoa," I call to Cyrus, sitting back as I give him a tug to slow him down so we can respect the vertical. This time he listens to me and slows his pace just enough, and then we're over the last jump and through the timers. It wasn't clean—and at times it wasn't that pretty—but we did it.

I fall on Cyrus's neck and hug him, relief washing over me in waves. We made it.

# Chapter Twelve

# Avalanche

After my ride, I have the typical post-course huddle with Trina, where she talks through all the highs and lows of the ride. Once she's said her piece, Alex is standing there at the edge of the schooling ring, waiting to take Cyrus back to the barn. I purposely lead Cyrus in the opposite direction, away from Alex, and begin walking him back myself. Distantly, Alex is calling for me, but I don't turn my head.

My heart is beating so hard, sweat pouring down my face and back, and all I want is to be back at the barns. I feel everyone's eyes on me as we walk back, and I have the audacity to urge Cyrus into a trot, to get back quicker. I know I should let him rest after such a huge event, but I can't. All I can think about is being in the safety of the barn.

After what seems like an eternity, we reach the temporary barns. I throw myself off of Cyrus and hurry him into the stall, taking off his bridle to let him drink, and uncinching his girth. I toss my tack into a pile in the corner of Cyrus's stall, and then wedge myself beside it as Cyrus drinks from his water bucket.

Cyrus swings his dripping nose to my helmet, nuzzling me curiously. As the water from his mouth drips onto my lap, the tears finally, finally come.

When you're in pain for so long, you just learn to build walls. Shut down the pain. But with it, you shut down everything else too—the joy, the hope, the anticipation. All the feelings go into the ground, buried. You become a shell of a person, which is an easier way to live if you don't want to be in pain.

But the problem is, when you start to feel something—even if it's positive—it *all* comes busting out. The pain, the heartache, the disappointment you've stuffed behind walls. It rushes out like a tsunami and you're caught in its undertow.

It's like an avalanche I'd been holding back for a full year that I was finally too weak to hold back anymore. The sobs shake my body, tighten my chest, and violently rip their way out of me.

Cyrus lowers his head and I hold him, my face in his forelock, my tears mingling with his sweaty coat. My wonderful, perfect Cyrus, who was never supposed to be mine in the first place. Anya's horse. Anya's perfect horse, perfect for Anya. And where is she now?

At home—forever in bed—her body is still here, but whatever's left of her soul is gone.

And me? Why am I the one intact? The bumbling daughter, the inconsistent sister, the anxious rider. Why was I the one who got to finish the Grand Prix?

I don't even hear the stall door open, but I sense Alex's presence the moment he enters the stall. He doesn't say anything, just simply sits beside me, his back against the stall wall. Cyrus, the traitor, pulls away from me and muzzles Alex, who of course has mints in his pocket. Cyrus's ears perk as the mint wrapper crinkles in Alex's hand.

"Good boy, Cy," he says as he strokes Cyrus's cheek. "You did so good out there, *mi amiguito*. Your rider here must be crying tears of joy."

I snort, an ugly sound filled with snot and tears. I look around for someplace to wipe my nose—my $500 jacket not exactly an option—and Alex hands me the rag from his pocket.

"Thanks," I say, my voice mercilessly nasally.

"Welcome," Alex says, mocking my congestion.

I can't help but laugh, even though it sounds like another snort.

"Now," Alex says, addressing Cyrus, "how many more mints do you need before you tell me why she's crying?"

I laugh again and blow my nose into the rag. The tears keep falling, but they're tamer now, less violent than before. Alex sits in silence with me for a long time, both of us stroking opposite sides of Cyrus's face. And he just stands there, letting us find comfort and solace in him.

This, I know from experience, is why people use animals, and especially horses, as therapy animals. They absorb your pain. They're patient listeners, statuesque in their faithfulness, calm in your storm. How did I get to be so lucky as to be sitting here with a horse this amazing?

Oh, right. My sister had to almost die. In some ways, she has a fate worse than death. Alive, but not living.

"I stole Cyrus from her," I finally croak out.

Alex is fiddling with Cyrus's forelock, and he pauses. "Is that true, Cyrus? Were you stolen?"

Cyrus blows air loudly through his nostrils, as if on cue, right into Alex's lap.

"I didn't think so," Alex says.

"If Anya were here, she'd be riding Cyrus, not me."

Alex finally turns to me, taking in my disheveled, tear-streaked face. He pulls my hand into his two rough hands and says, ever so gently, "That's the thing though, Mila. She's not here, is she?"

I shake my head, closing my eyes as more tears spill out, dripping onto the fresh shavings below. "No," I squeak. "She's not."

The sobs come again, wracking my body, as Alex holds me and Cyrus hovers above us, protecting us from the outside world. And I just cry, and cry. I sob for all that Anya has lost, all that I lost, and all that I've taken from Anya—things I desperately wanted, like a horse like Cyrus—and things I didn't, like more pressure from my dad.

"She should have been out there today."

"I know." Alex sighs, squeezing my hand. "But the thing is, you can't make up for her not being here by throwing away what you've been given. What does Anya want you to do? Not show Cyrus? Not relish the greatest gift someone could pass on to you?"

"I don't know what she wants," I say honestly.

"Well, maybe it's time to talk to her and find out."

Finally, Cyrus moves away from us and goes to nibble on some left-over hay. I think about Anya's room—or rather, her door, the part I'm most familiar with these days. Behind that door, my frail, crippled, depressed sister. What would she say to me? Would she rail at me for abandoning her? Would she envy my health, when she had none? If I were in her position, I don't think I could find it in my heart to be happy for my kid sister living her best life, while my broken body wasted away in bed.

"Hey, Mila?"

I glance up at Alex.

"Just because your sister's life is forever altered doesn't mean that you need to alter yours out of guilt. Live your life, not in spite of Anya, but because of her."

On my way home, I'm reliving every aspect of my ride, and the talk with Alex after. I realize that even though we talked for a long time after the course, neither one of us acknowledged the kiss I gave him before I went into the ring. Which is probably for the best.

Somehow, despite the fact that I survived the course, I'm still picturing Cyrus and me falling. He flips over the water jump, sending me face first into the water. A rail catches between his legs, and he falls on his neck, my head slamming into the ground. The images suffocate me. Why can't I get my thoughts under control? Why am I like this? Why can't I just be happy?

And, on top of it all, I know I need to talk to Anya. And I'm just not ready.

Alex is right—I need to just get it over with and talk it out with her. But just like with the Grand Prix, I'm only picturing our conversation ending in disaster.

I'm halfway back to Weston when I get a phone call from Michael.

"Hey, where are you?" he asks, and my stomach drops. I forgot we had plans to go out. How in the world could I forget?

"I, uh, had to go home," I lie. "Something came up with Anya."

"Oh, okay." He sighs. "That's lame. I was looking forward to going out with you."

"Me too," I say weakly. "How about next weekend? Unless you want to come down here? I just kinda got this thing going with my dad until I get my applications in, he cut off my credit card. So I don't have a lot of extra money for gas."

"Oh wow, that's...harsh."

"No kidding."

"Well, I can come to you, then. How about tomorrow night? I have a four o'clock class but I'm free after that."

"Sure, I'd like that."

We hang up, and I shake my head. If I knew that all I needed to do to keep Michael around was compete in a Grand Prix, I would've done that a while ago.

Or would I have?

When I get home, my mom is in the kitchen, pacing. She practically jumps through the roof when I walk in.

"Mila! Thank God!" She hugs me. "I just got a call from Yeva. *Babusya*," my grandmother, "is in the hospital."

"What? Oh my gosh, what happened?"

She presses her lips together, and she's fighting back tears when she says, "Stroke."

I pull her back into a hug and we're gripping each other like the other person is the only thing anchoring us to the ground. "I'm so sorry, Mom."

"Me too," she says, swiping tears from her cheeks. "I'm going to go down there." She gestures at the small suitcase by the front door.

"Where is she?"

"Palmetto." I nod and she continues, "I need you to take care of Anya."

My throat constricts and I flash back to my conversation with Alex. It's like Fate is forcing us to talk, though it's literally the last thing I want to do right now—waltz into her room and confess that I took *her* Grand Prix horse that she couldn't even finish *one* course with and did what she couldn't do. I feel nauseous just thinking about it, which in turn makes me woozy because I'm pretty sure I'm double-negative when it comes to my calories today.

My mom hugs me again, rubbing my back. "I know the second sister gets the grease," she says. And I just shake my head at my mom's bizarre sayings.

"And what does the first sister get?"

"The bacon."

"Huh."

My mom leaves, handing off Anya's monitor to me, and I make myself two peanut butter and jelly sandwiches, my mouth watering the whole time, and start eating them on my way up the stairs. I shower off and then I'm standing in front of Anya's door, which feels impenetrable.

I've been out here for at least five minutes when Anya's voice calls out, "I know you're out there, Mila."

I don't know whether to laugh, or cry. I do neither, I simply open the door, and come in to face my sister—awake—for the first time in months in her bedroom. We've had our monthly family dinners, where we've made polite chit-chat, but I haven't come into her room while she's cognizant in a long time. My heart is so heavy with guilt, I barely make it over the threshold.

Anya is sitting up in her bed, and there are pillows all around her, holding her up. Her dark brown hair is brushed around her face, trailing down her shoulders. It's the first time in days I've seen her blue eyes open, and they look almost vacant. *Is that even my sister?*

"Hey."

"Hey."

"Heard about *Babusya?*"

"Yeah. Terrible."

"Yeah."

We sort of stare–but–not–stare at each other, and I shuffle into the room and flop onto mom's cot. It's thin and crinkly, and for the first time I wonder if my mom is punishing herself for something. She really should be sleeping on a regular bed.

"What are we watching tonight?" I ask.

Anya shrugs, except she doesn't. She can't move her shoulders, but her eyebrows kind of shrug.

"*Heartland?*" I suggest, eager to get over the talking part and on to the staring–at–the–screen part of our time together. Heartland used to be *our* show that we watched every Thursday night.

"Mom and I finished it."

"Oh." I don't tell her that Monica and I finished it, too.

I flip through Netflix, and we make very nebulous comments like, 'that looks solid,' or 'I could watch that,' until we decide on *Love is Blind*, a reality dating TV show about strangers who talk—and fall in love and *propose*—without ever seeing each other. Then, once they're engaged, they meet up for four weeks before going to the altar.

At first as we watch, we're both pretty silent. I wonder if Anya's breathing has always been so loud, or if that's a symptom of her paralysis. I try not to glance at her every few seconds, but I do, only to find her staring straight ahead, mouth clenched in a hard line.

But then, halfway through the episode, Anya seems to forget herself and says, "Oh my gosh, that girl's voice is *so* annoying."

"I know, if I heard her voice in one of the pods, I'd literally hightail it outta there."

She snorts, a habit that is very similar to my own ladylike grunts, and it knocks something loose in me.

"Anya?"

"Yeah?"

"I'm sorry."

She glances over at me, and I expect my sister to have tears in her eyes or to look pitifully at me, but instead she's furious.

"Are you serious right now, Mila?"

I'm completely taken aback. "Um, yes?"

"You think you can just straggle in here for the first time in *months,* mumble an apology, and think that makes up for everything?"

"No?" But, honestly, I feel pathetic because, yes, I did kind of expect that. Because my sister has always been there to catch me when I fall, and I fell hard this time. Except she did too, just harder. "I'm sorry, I wish I knew what else I could say."

"No, you don't get to say that. You don't get to think that that's enough."

"I know it's not enough."

"Do you, though?"

"I just, couldn't, face you. Not when I'm perfectly healthy and living my life and you're stuck here forever."

"Oh, I'm sorry, *you couldn't handle my pain?* Is that it? Well I'm so sorry I went and got paralyzed. How hard that must have been for you."

"I know it's nowhere near as hard as for you, but it has been really hard."

"Boo freaking hoo." Then she's silent, her face as stony as Mount Rushmore, and we go back to watching the show, though I'm confident neither of us is really watching.

The reality of how I've hurt Anya is crashing into me, and my insides are aching like I've just been flattened. And, in a way, I have. How could I just think that Anya and I could pick up where we left off just by me saying, 'I'm sorry'?

After a while, Anya says, "You know that I can't move, right? I literally can't get out of bed and find you? So if you don't come to me, I don't see you." She starts crying then, and I feel like crap. "I'm so alone, Mila. You left me alone," she spits at me.

This time, instead of staying glued to the cot, I get up onto Anya's bed and wrap my arms around her. "I'm so sorry," I say, and then the tears are coming again. Anya's tears are streaking down her face, falling into my hair, down my arms, mingling with my own tears. "I'm so, so, sorry," I keep saying. "You deserved so much better from me."

"I know I did," she weeps.

And we're sitting there, both of us sobbing truly ugly sobs, while Jessica from *Love is Blind* is saying in her squeaky voice, "Like, integrity is everything to me. I'm definitely...super...Christian." And her date, a guy named Mark responds by saying, "Holy $#*!, we're the same #@$%*&! version."

And then we're both laughing through the tears and through the snot. Because, *who says that?* And for a moment it feels like we're back to being Anya and Mila again.

I stumble out of the bed and grab a tissue, holding it up to Anya's nose for her to blow. I wipe her tears and adjust her hair out of her face. "I know that nothing I say can make up for me not being there for you these past few months, but will you let me try to make things right?"

Anya nods tearfully, and for a moment she feels like pre-accident Anya, I almost forget about the paralysis. I lean my forehead against hers and say, "*Ya tebya lubloo, sestra.*"

She kisses my cheek and says, "I love you too."

I settle on the bed next to her, curling under the covers, and sigh. Because, wow, I feel like a weight the size of Cyrus has been lifted from me.

"You have a lot of catching up to do," she tells me, "because I really need someone other than mom to live vicariously through."

I laugh, but what she's saying smacks of too much truth to laugh too hard.

"Well, me and Michael broke up."

She shakes her head, like she already knew—probably my mom told her. "I totally thought you guys were going to get married."

"Me too." I toy with the edge of the blanket, flipping it back and forth. "I guess there's a chance we still might." I tell her about his reasoning for breaking up with me, and my cockeyed plan for winning him back over—to compete in a Grand Prix, show him I'm back to being Old Mila. I don't, however, mention that I've already ridden in the Grand Prix.

"Well, I'll be honest, Mila, your plan sucks. You shouldn't be competing for anyone else but yourself."

I bristle at her words. What other cards do I have to play?

"But I will say I'm happy to hear you've been moping around without me."

I arch a brow, thinking that maybe Alex was wrong about thinking Anya wanted me to live my life to the fullest, even if she wasn't living her life. "Really?"

"I mean, yeah. I thought you just moved on and forgot about me."

I reach across the bed and take her hand. I actually don't even know if she can feel it when I squeeze her fingers in mine. "I could never. I've been utterly miserable. So miserable, in fact, that the boy I was in love with broke up with me."

She cackles, and then stops herself. "Wait, *was?*"

It's not until she points it out that I realize what I've said. I can't stop to think about whether it's true or not. Before I can think better of it, I launch into a long narrative about the past few weeks with Alex.

"Wow. Just, wow." She juts her chin at her bedside stand. "Can I have some water?" I grab the glass from her nightstand and point the straw into her lips and wait while she drinks. When she's done, she pushes the straw out with her tongue and I put the cup back. "Now that is interesting. Definitely didn't see that coming, *malenka sestra.*"

I smile when she calls me little sister in Ukrainian; it warms a part of me that has seemed dead for a long time. Once we catch up on the nitty gritty details of my love life, we go back to watching *Love is Blind*—mocking Jessica, swooning over Cameron and Lauren, cringing when Carlton isn't forthcoming with Diamond. And it's the highest high I've had in months—even better than jumping in the Grand Prix, better than my boat ride with Michael, better than anything I can imagine.

Eventually, we fall asleep, both of us in Anya's bed like when we were kids, and for the first time in a year I only have good dreams.

# Chapter Thirteen

---

# Milly Vanilly

The next day, Anya and I binge the entire season one of *Love is Blind*. It feels like we're *almost* back to being us, except there's an emptiness in Anya's eyes whenever she thinks I'm not looking. Plus, the caretaking for Anya is no joke. I have to feed Anya, give her water, and, most interesting of all, take her to the bathroom, which includes a suppository insertion a few minutes beforehand.

"How does mom do this every day?" I grunt as I try to position her on the toilet, while she's a complete deadweight on me.

"At this point, she's so strong, she tosses me around like she's Hulk."

"Huh." For some reason, this doesn't jive with my image of my very petite mother. But then again, no one has had to change more or make more sacrifices than she has since Anya's accident.

I hold Anya in place on the toilet, waiting for her to go. The worst part is the wiping, but Anya keeps making jokes and it makes it a thousand times better.

"Just preparing you for having kids," she says. "Wiping their butts is going to seem like a piece of cake in comparison."

I chuckle, grateful that she can at least fake having a sense of humor about this—it would be so much worse if we both felt awkward about it. By the time I get her back into the bed, I'm sweating like I just jumped in three back-to-back Grand Prix courses. Without a horse.

Before lunch, we FaceTime Mom and *Babusya*, and we're both relieved that she's looking so good. Mom assures us that the doctors said she's looking good and she'll be going home soon.

After I've fed Anya her lunch and downed mine, I know it's time to breach the subject I've been dreading ever since I walked through Anya's door.

"I, um, rode in a Grand Prix."

Anya looks at me, but I'm avoiding her gaze like the coward I am. "When?"

"Yesterday."

"Yesterday was your first time?"

I nod.

"Wow, I'm surprised you waited that long."

"Really?" I finally meet her eyes. She doesn't *look* upset.

"Yeah, I mean it's been your dream for forever, and then you're handed a fantastic Grand Prix horse. I thought you'd take Cyrus in a Grand Prix the second he was yours."

I'm staring at Anya, wide-eyed, because this is not at all what I expected this conversation to be like. Also, of all the people in the world who might understand my hesitation for not taking Cyrus in a Grand Prix, I thought Anya would totally get it.

"I haven't exactly wanted to ride him in a Grand Prix..."

"Wait, why?"

"Well, I mean, I have your accident in my head." I pick at a thread on her comforter as I debate how much to tell her, just how much her accident has affected me psychologically.

"Are you telling me you were scared to go in a Grand Prix?" Anya cocks an eyebrow at me.

"Well..." I shrug, knowing that 'scared' doesn't even begin to cover it. "Yeah."

Then Anya laughs. She actually laughs at me.

I'm completely and totally taken aback. And, also, defensive of the whole thing. Like, she may have been destroyed by the accident, but she didn't have to watch it happen. I did, and I relive it every day.

"I never thought you, Mila Fire-Eating Kozak, would be scared of anything. *Especially* this."

What can I say? How do I tell Anya I'm not the same Mila anymore? The whole conversation has me feeling hollow and very, very alone. If Anya can't understand what I'm going through, who can?

And then the tears are coming again, and it's like I'm making up for an entire year of not crying.

"Oh, Milochka, no." Anya's voice softens. And normally, this is the part where she'd throw her arms around me and hold me. But of course, she can't do that. And I just wish to God she could, because I need an Anya hug more than anything right now.

Instead, I curl up in her lap and weep.

"Oh, Mila, it's okay," she keeps saying, even though it's not at all okay and it will never be okay. Hearing my sister's reminder that I am not at all the person I used to be—it's decimating. I feel stripped, like someone pulled back all the walls I've put up over the past year only to find out there's nothing behind them.

Finally, when I've cried out all the tears I can muster, I sit up and wipe my face on my shirt. "I thought, I dunno, I thought you'd be upset or jealous or something. This just wasn't the response I was expecting."

Anya's looking at me like I'm as fragile as a Ming vase, and I want to remind her I'm not the paralyzed one. "Honestly, Mila, I'm surprised that my accident affected you so much. You've always been so resilient. Even as a kid, you would run into the freaking wall at full speed and just bounce right back up like nothing happened. When we first came to the States and we were so poor, you hardly noticed. I would be crying to Tato about not having the latest toy or gadget that my schoolmates had, and you would be in the corner making dolls out of paper napkins like you were the richest kid on the block." She laughs as if she's watching that young Mila right now. "You've always been that way, Milochka."

"Yeah, well, I'm definitely not that way anymore."

"Let's be real, though, you could have used a bit more caution in you. Maybe my accident saved you from doing something really stupid."

"Like riding in a Grand Prix? Oh, wait..."

She laughs, and I love seeing the glimmer in my sister's eyes, the one that was so diminished after the accident. The one I missed so much that I ran away from her. I take her hand in mine and tell her, "I'm glad you're not mad at me for taking Cyrus in a Grand Prix."

"Mila, *I gave him to you.* What do you think I thought you would do with him? Sell him for glue?"

I crinkle my nose at the glue thing. Too far, Anya. Too far. "I don't know."

"Let me tell you something: a person can feel two things at the same time. I can be devastated that I will never ride again, while also being deliriously happy that you get to fulfill your dream."

I nod, because what she's saying resonates with me in more ways than one. I think about my feelings for Michael, and whatever it is that's going on inside of me when it comes to Alex.

"Thanks, Anya." I squeeze her hand. "You really are the best sister ever."

"Oh, I know," she says with an eye roll, and I break out into a smile. "Now, on to more important matters. Should we see if Damien and Giannina actually say I do?"

"Oh my gosh, there's no way," I say as I flip the TV back on and snuggle up next to my sister.

Several hours later, I get a text from Michael: *Getting off on Royal Palm now.*

"Oh my gosh." I jump up. "I forgot I told Michael I would hang out with him tonight."

"What's the problem?"

"Well, I'm supposed to be taking care of you."

"I mean, you can still hang out with Michael. You could take the monitor downstairs in case I need anything. You could, I don't know, order in and sit out on the patio or something." She studies my face for a second. "Unless, of course, you don't *want* to hang out with Michael," she says slowly, hesitantly.

"No, I do. I do." In fact, it's pretty much the only thing I've wanted since he broke up with me six weeks ago. "Okay, yeah, I'll do that."

"We could watch a movie all together. I don't mind, if you need a buffer."

I nod, but internally cringe when I think about Michael's comment about how all we used to do was sit around and watch sad movies. That's definitely not an option.

"Ugh, I'm a mess," I say, looking down at my rumpled clothes.

"Hey, if he doesn't love you for exactly how you are, you don't need that in your life." But then she glances over at me and amends her statement. "Yeah, but maybe you should run a brush through your hair."

"Anya!" I groan as I rush from the room.

"Some concealer wouldn't be a bad idea, either!" she calls after me.

A few minutes later, Michael knocks at the door and I'm at least halfway presentable. But as soon as I open the door, I realize I've gotten it all wrong. Michael is dressed in his blue Tom Ford suit and is holding a huge bouquet of flowers.

"Oh," he says when I open the door in my yoga pants and t-shirt.

"What every girl wants to hear when a guy sees her," I snark as I take the flowers. While I'm reaching for them, Michael bends and kisses me on the cheek like it's the most normal thing in the world. And in an instant my body heats up, and I'm wishing I had put at least a little makeup on.

"I, uh, thought we were going to celebrate the Grand Prix thing."

"Sorry, my mom had to leave. My grandma's in the hospital. So I have to watch Anya." I beckon him inside and we make our way to the kitchen, where I rummage under the sink to find a vase.

"Oh, sorry. That...sucks."

"Yeah, it really does. I mean, about my grandma. Not about watching Anya. We've had a really good time, actually."

"That's good." He pulls his phone out of his pocket. "I just have to cancel our reservations. One sec."

I fill the vase with water and arrange the bouquet. It's absolutely stunning, with gigantic white roses offset by fragrant eucalyptus leaves and other greenery, along with sprigs of a tiny blue flower I don't recognize. The whole thing makes me anxious—which is really confusing, because a couple weeks ago, I would've been *thrilled* to have Michael show up at my door looking like a million bucks with flowers.

So why am I not happier?

I shake my head, thinking I'm just tired and emotionally drained from talking with Anya and taking care of her. Not to mention the Grand Prix I rode in yesterday, and staying up all night with Alex.

*Alex.*

The thought of him brings a pang of shame, but then Michael is in front of me with his boundless blue eyes saying, "Alright, that's done. What you wanna do?"

"We could order in. What are you in the mood for?"

"You choose, it's your night we're celebrating."

"Alright then," I say with a smile. "I could go for a Cuban steak."

Michael laughs mirthlessly and says, "You're into Cubans lately, huh?"

I glance up from my phone, where I was looking up the number for a local Cuban restaurant and say, "What's that supposed to mean?"

"I mean that Cuban guy you've been running around with."

"'Running around with'? Are you serious?" I put a hand on my hip. "What about you and Amber?"

Michael stuffs his hands in his pockets and at least has the decency to not look at me when he says, "That's nothing."

"*She* certainly doesn't think it's nothing."

"I know," he sighs.

"You shouldn't lead her on, Michael. It's not fair."

"I didn't come here for a lecture."

I really need a subject change, so I hand Michael my phone with the menu to the Cuban place that my family loves. We manage to avoid the topics of Amber and Alex the rest of the evening, and instead focus on the Grand Prix. It's enjoyable to go through the details of the whole course, and Michael is an enthusiastic listener. For the first time since my breakdown yesterday, I feel proud of what I've accomplished.

When our food is delivered, we go outside onto the patio and eat around the couch there.

"Tell me about USEF," I say casually.

"Ah," he says between bites, "so your dad told you?"

"He *is* my dad."

"Honestly?"

"No, lie to me."

He smirks at me, revealing one of his perfect dimples. "I kind of wanted to make my own way. Like not riding my mom's tailcoats, or your dad's or anyone else's."

"That makes sense."

"Really?"

"Yeah, it makes a lot of sense."

"Huh. I don't know why I thought you wouldn't get it."

"Why is that exactly?"

"Well, mostly 'cause you just fall in line whenever your dad tells you to do something."

"Hmm." I take another bite of my steak, trying to mentally smooth down the hurt that Michael's comment ruffled within me. "So what are you gonna do for them?"

"I'll be the assistant regional manager for the Southern circuit."

"You mean the assistant *to* the regional manager?"

He smirks again, and it makes me smile.

"I'll get you one of those Office shirts."

"Gee, thanks."

I'm shoveling bites of rice and the citrusy steak into my mouth when Michael surprises me and snaps a picture. "You really gotta work on your table manners," he laughs.

"You know, you're not the first guy to tell me that in recent days."

Something flashes in his eyes, and I wonder if he's a little jealous, but he quickly covers it up and jokes, "I'm sure there's, like, YouTube videos or online courses you could take to help you."

I roll my eyes and take another bite, chewing loudly. Michael laughs and shakes his head at me, but I'm thinking about Alex again and wondering why I feel like I'm betraying him right now.

Later, Michael shows me a new artist he's really into called Nic D and when one song comes on—"Pretty Faces"—Michael's doing this white boy rap-sing thing that's got me cracking up. "The way I love you, miss you, always wanna kiss you/I don't need to save you, you don't need a rescue." The more I laugh, the more into it he gets. And that's the thing about Michael—he's a ham. So now he's standing up, swinging his arm in a circle Elvis-style as he pretends to sing into a microphone. "And I'm still livin', kickin', makin' bad decisions/lookin', cookin', dirty up the kitchen."

After the second chorus, I've caught on to the song and now I'm singing along. Michael grabs my hand, but before he can twirl me around, the song ends abruptly.

"Wait, is that really the end of the song?"

Michael grabs his phone and shouts, "REPLAY!" and plays the song again. As soon as it starts, he's twirling me around like a maniac and we're both laughing. He takes another picture while he spins me and I make a face at him. This song, this moment, is so Michael and it takes me back to Old Mila. It makes me think I can still be her.

After we eat, we change and jump in the pool. I situate Anya's monitor next to the pool and put some music on low on the pool speakers. My dad put special speakers into the pool itself so when you go underwater, you hear the music there, too. Of course it sounds a little distorted, and Michael and I play a game where we go under water and try to interpret the lyrics. It's a little like playing a wacky game of telephone.

A song by Nic D called "Skin like summer" is on and it's Michael's turn. He pops out of the pool and says, "Is it 'have to have you, puff it'?"

I laugh, "Puff it? Is it a song about drugs?"

"Love can be a drug," he says as he splashes me. I mock-scream and dart under the water, but he catches me around the waist, pulling me up. "For your mockery, I sentence you to three dunks under the pool."

"No—" but my protests are cut off by Michael submerging me.

After three thorough dunkings, he releases me. "Your punishment has been served."

"I'll say." I roll my eyes.

"Something tells me you're not just referring to the soaking you just got."

I give him a *'ya think?'* look. He sighs deeply, and we're both just treading there, the reflection of the water and pool lights rippling off his clean shaven jaw. He looks so boyish right now—his blue eyes like the waters of the Caribbean, his wet hair falling around his eyes, water droplets pooling on his sun-kissed skin.

"It's been pretty torturous for me, too," he says finally.

"You do know *you* broke up with me, right?"

He exhales loudly again and then slowly lowers himself under the water, and I take that to mean he *does* take responsibility. When he comes back up, he pushes back his hair so it's out of his face and then says, "I'm sorry, Mila."

I nod, because I'm not yet ready to say, 'I forgive you.' But it's a start. "You know, in the future, you can just talk to someone about what's bothering you *before* you break up with them."

He treads closer to me so that we're only inches from each other, our limbs knocking into each other as we try to stay afloat. "Are you referring to our future, or my future with someone else?"

"I don't know," I answer honestly.

At the end of the night, I walk Michael to the front door. "I still want to take you out as a celebration for the Grand Prix."

"This was enough for me," I tell him. "The flowers are really nice, too."

"I know, but you deserve it all."

My heart stutters, and the look Michael's giving me makes me think he's about to kiss me. But when he leans down, I give him my cheek, which shocks me more than it does him. Because isn't this what my whole plan was for? Didn't I just compete in the Grand Prix for this exact moment? And now that it's here, I'm turning away from it?

He doesn't miss a beat, though. He kisses my cheek and then laughs. "I see how it is, Milly. I'll win you back over."

I roll my eyes when he calls me 'Milly'—it's got to be the worst nickname of all time, ever. Early on when we first started dating, I mentioned the 'Milly' thing to Michael, but he never really got it. And it's unfortunately persisted, apparently even past our breakup.

"Goodnight, Michael."

He winks at me and gives me his killer smile that sends a thrill up my spine. "Night, Mila."

And then, he's gone and I'm feeling more confused than ever. Wasn't this everything I wanted?

# Chapter Fourteen

# Let's Talk About Poop, Baby

I spend the rest of the night dissecting with Anya my entire time with Michael while I trim, file, and paint Anya's nails. I have to confess, I'm not that great at it, but Anya can't exactly complain about it, can she? And, to her credit, she doesn't.

"Do you think he thinks you're back together?"

"I honestly don't know. He literally went to kiss me—would he have done that if we were still broken up?"

Anya glances up at the ceiling, her eyes darting back and forth like she's really trying to figure this out for me. "I really have no idea."

"I mean, Michael definitely can be the fly-by-the-seat-of-his-pants type," I say, thinking that he probably didn't overthink the kiss—he just did it.

"I'm not sure it's the *seat* part he's flying by."

We both crack up at that, and there's a warmth building in my chest as I soak in this moment with Anya. So normal, so wonderful.

"He's moving to Kentucky in a couple months to work for USEF," I tell her.

"Hmm." I glance up at Anya, trying to figure out if the *hmm* means 'long distance relationships never work, why even try' or 'that's an interesting wrinkle but you can figure it out.' I can't decipher her thoughts, though.

"Before all of this, I felt like I had to win him back ASAP, you know. But now, I'm not so sure..."

As if on cue, my phone buzzes.

"It's Alex."

Anya squeals. "The drama continues! This is better than *Love is Blind!*"

I turn the phone around to show her what he sent—a picture of Cyrus, his perky gray ears pointing forward, his nose tilting forward as if he's about to nibble a treat off of Alex's hand. And a text that says, *This guy's missing you.*

"Ah!" Anya shrieks. "He misses you!"

"I'm pretty sure he meant *Cyrus* misses me."

Anya rolls her eyes. "Don't be intentionally naive, *sestra.*"

I'm not sure how to respond, so I send a smiley face. Alex responds immediately, sending back his own smiley face. Then: *Goodnight, Mila Kozak.*

"Ugh," I fall back onto the bed, clutching my phone. "Why is it so hot when guys use your full name?"

"He didn't even say it, he just texted it."

"I know, but I can hear it in his voice and it is sexy as all get out."

Anya snickers and then, in her pragmatic way she goes, "Alright, let's say you're on *Love is Blind.* Which guy would you connect with most in the pods?"

I think about it for a few minutes. I enjoy talking with both Alex and Michael. Obviously, I've spent a lot more time talking with Michael than Alex since we dated for so long, but arguably Alex is the more considerate conversationalist. Michael makes me laugh hysterically, though.

"I'd have long, deep conversations with Alex, and flirt like crazy with Michael."

"So basically Michael would be your Barnett and Alex would be your...Cameron?" She raises a perfectly arched eyebrow at me, and I realize mom must be keeping up with plucking Anya's eyebrows, because obviously Anya's not doing it.

I laugh at her *Love is Blind*-esque analysis. "I'm not ready to go that far."

"Uh huh." She smiles mischievously.

It's in this moment that my brain unearths something I would've given my left pinky finger to forget: before Michael and I dated, Anya and Michael made out one night. And didn't tell me about it until Michael and I had been together for almost a year. A new wave of bitterness crashes over me. It's been over two years since it happened, but remembering it now feels as if it happened yesterday. And it makes me mistrust Anya, and Michael.

A minute later, I get a text from Monica: *You + Michael = ??*

Me: *what do you mean?*

Then she sends me a screenshot of Michael's Instagram, where he just posted pictures from our evening together—including one I didn't know he took of me getting out of the pool. I immediately open the app and find the post to show Anya.

"*Matinko*," she whistles. "This boy is marking his territory."

"You think so?"

"Oh, I *know* so." She thinks for a second. "Did Michael start showing more interest in you again after he saw you with Alex a few times?"

"Yeah..."

"Well, there you have it."

"Is that a bad thing?"

"Only if *you* think it is." She clicks her tongue. "He probably just realized what he was missing once he saw you with Alex."

"Huh," I say, not sure if I'm convinced. I should be happy that Michael and I are advancing like this, but instead I feel uneasy. A huge part of me is relieved that Alex isn't on Instagram, and yet, I untag myself in the pictures even though I don't totally know why. Anya is talking to me, so I don't have time to process it all.

"Okay, here's another one for you: you're in the pods, they both propose, you say yes to both. Then you're in the reveal hallway and the doors open. Which one are you happier to see?"

"Like, which one am I more attracted to initially?"

Anya does her eye-shrug thing and says, "However you want to interpret that question is fine."

"Okay," I say, dragging out the word. I close my eyes and imagine the reveal doors opening. First, it's Michael, then Alex, behind the doors. I think about Michael in his Tom Ford suit, the dark blue making his eyes like the stormy ocean. The way he smiles at me like I'm the only girl in the world. Those *dimples*.

And then there's Alex. I think about him when he dressed up for our date in his bomber jacket, the way his white shirt fitted perfectly across his muscular chest and how it contrasted with his tanned skin. Those dark, black-hole eyes of his that pull me in and I can't even fight against them.

Oh Mi-ami. "They're both just really different."

"You'll figure it out, Mila." Anya says it so confidently, I want to believe it, but I feel more muddled than ever. And remembering the kiss between Anya and Michael only makes me more confused. Should I have even forgiven him for not telling me? Should I have forgiven *her* for not telling me? A mess of emotions swirls in my stomach, making me feel nauseous and alone.

A few weeks ago, all I'd wanted is exactly what was happening—I was dying to win over Michael. But now I'm not sure that's what I want anymore.

My mom got back on Wednesday afternoon, with reports that *Babusya* was back home and stable. I agreed to go out on Wednesday night with Michael after riding Cyrus at Zen Elite. And, because I'm the worst person in the world, I also made plans with Alex for Sunday night.

As I'm on my way to meet up with Michael, I get a frantic call from Trina. Before we hang up, I'm squealing into a U-turn on Lake Worth Road and racing to the barn. Trina meets me, mascara streaked around her brown eyes.

"It's the feed," she says as I rush out of my mom's car. She had gas, I didn't.

"What happened with the feed?"

Trina sighs heavily, running her fingers across her eyelids. "It was moldy. There's multiple cases of colic. It's all hands on deck right now." She grabs hold of me, holding me back from running to Cyrus's stall. "I'm so sorry, Mila. You know how diligent we are about this kind of thing. I already have a call into the feed store to see if they've had any other complaints. I checked the bags. None of them are anywhere close to the expiration date, nothing in the feed room was wet. I don't understand how it could have happened."

I squeeze Trina's arm, and I know I should say something like, *it's okay* or *I understand*. But right now, I can't honestly say either of those things. I simply nod and turn toward the barn.

"Dr. Canton is with Cyrus," Trina says from behind me. "He...understands the importance."

The importance? The importance of the only living being I can truly trust with my whole self in the depths of a potentially deadly episode of colic? Anxiety clenches at my lungs, squeezing them until I can barely take a breath.

When I reach Cyrus's stall, Dr. Canton is listening to his bloated stomach with a stethoscope. Cyrus is in the corner of the stall, head low, eyelids drooping. The sight of him makes me feel weak and dizzy.

The vet is a thin, graying man with deft, calloused hands. I hold my breath as I wait for him to say something, anything. Down the hall, I sense Alex's presence before I even see him. He approaches quietly from behind me, placing a tentative hand on my lower back, and before he steps fully into the stall, I whirl into his arms.

A sob wracks my throat, and his long arms hold me against his chest. "He'll be okay, Mila. We're doing everything we can," he murmurs into my hair. I want to hide, to burrow myself in Alex's arms and not come out until this whole episode is past.

But then I remember Trina and Dr. Canton, standing only feet from where I'm crying all over Alex, and I pull back, suddenly embarrassed by my display of emotion. I wipe my cheeks and nod. "Yeah, I know you are."

The vet draws away from Cyrus and glances at me. "It's definitely colic, very severe." He sighs. And it seems like that's all everyone can do right now—sigh. Deeply. "We have a few options. I can give him a painkiller called Banamine, which I highly recommend. We can also administer mineral oil through a nasogastric tube, which will act like a laxative and help pass the moldy food faster."

"Are there any risks with that?"

"Well, if you don't know what you're doing with a nasogastric tube, you could risk it going down the wrong pipe." He smiles mirthlessly at me. "But don't worry, that's not a concern here. If that doesn't work, we'll have to bring him into the clinic for surgery."

"Surgery?" I say feebly.

I glance at Trina and Alex; I can tell they're both trying to keep their expressions neutral, but are failing. They look as worried as I feel.

"I want to do whatever we can for him."

"Okay, my dear, I'll get the Banamine and the tube." He squeezes my shoulder as he leaves the stall. "Alex, can you get a bucket of warm water?"

Alex nods and leaves the stall, and I rush to Cyrus's head, holding it softly in my arms.

"I'm so sorry, big guy," I whisper to him, my forehead against the broad part of his head. "We're going to get you through this." My throat is thick with emotion and it takes effort to push out the words.

"I'm going to go check on the others," Trina says. "Honey, Foxley and Julius are all colicking too, and we're keeping an eye on the rest."

I don't know if I reply to her or not; I'm too focused on the horse in front of me. Cyrus is so still, it's completely unnerving. I'm so sure that I can channel some of my strength, my health, into him. I lay my palms flat on his cheeks and pray.

*Please don't leave me,* I tell him.

We stand there, foreheads touching, my incantation repeating in my head like a broken record, until Dr. Canton and Alex return. The vet hands Alex a huge coil of tubing to place in the bucket of warm water, and I choke down my question: is that thing *really* going down my horse's throat?

I hold Cyrus's head as the vet gives him the Banamine injection into a vein in his neck. He rubs his neck where the injection has gone in and grabs the tube. My stomach twists as he uncoils the tubing, laying it onto his shoulders, and then he lubricates the outside.

As Dr. Canton pushes the tube into Cyrus's nostril, Cy is shaking his head. I hold his halter, keeping him as steady as I possibly can, but when I can't keep him still, Alex comes to the other side of Cyrus's head to help. The deeper the tube goes into Cyrus's nose, the more I have to fight the gag building in my throat. I grip his halter and close my eyes. When I feel the tube pass through the part of Cyrus neck that's touching my shoulder, I do gag. No one acknowledges it—or maybe they don't even notice—and I'm able to keep down my lunch, but just barely.

Once the tube is in, the vet puts his mouth to the tube and sucks on it to check that it went into Cyrus's stomach and not his lungs. When he's convinced it's in the right place, he attaches a pump to the part of the tube he's holding and places it into the bucket of water. Slowly, he pumps water into Cyrus's stomach and suctions it out. With each suction, a few pieces of grain come with the water.

"That's good," Dr. Canton says. "This way we're keeping at least some of the bad grain from going through his system."

Alex and I are both stroking Cyrus's side and murmuring to him, but Cyrus doesn't seem to even notice. He's so statuesque that it's completely freaking me out. Because this is Cyrus we're talking about—he's never held this still in his life.

After going through two buckets of water, the vet begins pumping the mineral oil down Cyrus's throat. When he's done and he's taking the tube out, I have to close my eyes to keep from gagging again. Anya would be ashamed of my weak stomach. And then I realize Anya doesn't know about Cyrus—he is still partially hers, even if she can't ride him anymore. I grab my phone to text her, but it's dead. It's at that point I remember my plans with Michael. He doesn't even know where I am or what's going on, and I certainly don't want to ask Alex to borrow his phone for *that*. I resolve to ask Trina—privately—to text Michael for me so he doesn't think I've blown him off.

Dr. Canton gives us instructions—don't let him roll; don't leave him alone; if he starts pawing, walk him; call him if he gets worse—and then he goes to check on the other horses.

Alex and I sort of hover around Cyrus, despite the vet's instructions, I can tell we both feel unsure of what to do or not do right that second. He seems so fragile, I'm almost afraid to touch him. A few minutes later, though, he starts really moving for the first time since I got there. He goes into this position like he's going to pee, with his hind legs stretched out. He's making a low groaning sound like he's trying to push something out, but he's stuck.

"Maybe we should walk him," Alex suggests.

We slowly circle the barn, and we discuss the moldy feed and the rampant colic.

"Trina's right, we're meticulous about the feed. She's got a whole system of when feed comes in, marking the date and using the bags in order of expiration so we don't encounter something like this."

"I believe you guys. It's just, how did it happen? Even if it was moldy when it was delivered, why did no one catch it before they fed it to all of the horses?"

"I don't know." He sighs and rubs a hand over his tired face. "Trina will get to the bottom of it and make sure it doesn't happen again."

I nod, but all I'm thinking is, *what if it's too late?*

As we walk, Alex starts talking to me about seemingly anything and everything that pops into his head. I'm sure he can tell how anxious I am, and honestly, I'm so grateful he's here to distract me. I'd be a total mess if I had to deal with this by myself. I mean, let's be real, I'm still a total mess.

He's telling me about the latest book he's reading and, wow, this guy has a really eclectic taste in books. Right now he's reading *The Monsanto Papers*, a nonfiction work about a legal case against the company that manufactures RoundUp. It's fascinating and also horrifying.

"It just seems like there's always a reason to not use one product or another," I say. "This one gives you cancer, that one makes you sprout a second head. Can you trust anything these days?"

"Yeah, you can really get your head in knots if you think about it too much."

I want to tell him I've got my head in knots, and it's *not* because of Monsanto, but instead I tell him all about *Love is Blind*, detailing each of the couples. He's clearly intrigued by the dynamics, and at first he's asking which couples end up saying I do, but he stops me.

"Wait, if any of them say no, I don't want to know."

"Really?"

"I can't handle that; I'm too much of an optimist. I'd rather think they all made it."

"After everything you've been through, you consider yourself an optimist?"

He shrugs as if to say, 'what can I tell you?' but I can't let it go. "Don't you feel like once you've been through something so traumatic, it makes you afraid something like that will happen again?"

"Sure, yeah, that's part of it. But I also think it makes you more present, more able to be grateful for the things or people you do have."

"Huh."

"I mean, look at me," he says, waving a hand at himself. "I'm shooting my shot with the most beautiful girl I've ever met," and I'm blushing because I realize he's referring to *me*, "and, hey, I may not be winning right now, but you're not running away screaming either, are you?"

"There's the optimist," I say, laughing, but I'm thinking about Anya's question to me—if the guys were in the pods, who would I want to talk to more? I surprise myself by thinking, *You* are *winning, Alex.*

Later, we're back in the stall and I'm struggling to stay awake.

"You could sleep," Alex says. "I can stay up with him."

I shake my head; I couldn't leave Cyrus. "You're worse at staying up than I am. I've just been up with Anya all week."

"So, you guys talked?"

I nod and smile up at him. "It was great."

He smiles back at me and it lights up the whole stall. "I knew it would be."

I tell him about our conversation—at least, I tell him about the parts that don't involve *him*.

After we fall into a comfortable silence that leads to me almost falling asleep, I sit up and ask, "You got anything interesting on your phone? Games or anything like that?"

He shrugs. "You could look." He hands me his phone and I take this as a good sign. What guy just hands over his phone to a girl, carte blanche? On his home screen, there's a note saved called 'business ideas.'

"Can I look at this?"

"Sure." But I can feel him tense as I open it. I decide I'm going to be encouraging, no matter what the ideas are, but it turns out I don't even need to fake it.

"You have some really good ideas here, Alex!"

"You sound surprised."

"I guess I shouldn't be, you're smart."

"I'm glad you've bought the charade." He says charade like a British person, with a soft second a.

"You couldn't pull a *charade*," I say charade correctly, "if you were paid a million dollars."

"You wound me, Mila."

"It's a compliment. You're honest. I like that."

Alex leans his head back on the stall wall, his eyes on me. "Are you saying you like me?"

I think about the repercussions of answering his question honestly, and, after a beat, I reply, "Yes, I do."

He smiles, and it's bashful and perfect. After a few moments of his eyes on me, enfolding me into their depths, I break off and return to his list.

"Wow, I love this idea," I say, pointing at the third item in his list: 'rider subscription service with new gear, apparel, horse treats, etc.'

"I thought that was a good idea, and it could be a way for newer companies to break into the marketplace."

I get to idea number seven and start cracking up. "Alex, this is hilarious. 'Chemical compound to spray on dog poop to make it disappear?'"

He shrugs, but he's smiling. "You only need to step in dog poop one time to think the idea's a good one."

"That's true. As long as it's environmentally friendly, I'm down for it." I keep scrolling. "Oh, I like this one—a frisbee version of Top Golf? That sounds super fun."

"That's one of my favorites. It just would take a lot of capital. Capital I definitely don't have right now."

"I get that." I keep reading all the way to the bottom. The last idea: therapy barn for quad/paraplegics. The idea makes me feel all sorts of things, but I don't have a chance to tell Alex about it because Trina pokes her head in, looking about as weary as I feel.

"How's he doing?"

"Good," I tell her. "He stopped pawing after we walked him, but he hasn't pooped yet so we might need to walk him again."

She gives us a thumbs up and disappears as quickly as she came.

"Are you hungry?" Alex asks. In response, my stomach gives a small roar. His eyes widen and then he laughs. "I guess that answers it." He stands up and puts his hand out for me. "What if one of us walks him and the other grabs some food?"

"Good idea. I'll walk him if that's okay." I look over at Cyrus, who's hanging his head low. "I don't want to leave him."

"You got it, boss."

He goes to turn away, but I catch his hand. "Hey, um." I glance up at him, unsure of how he'll respond to what I'm about to say. "Can you not, y'know, call me that?"

He takes a step closer to me, a small smile playing on his lips. "What would you like me to call you?" And something about the way he's saying it sounds more like 'where would you like me to kiss you?' and suddenly there's a warmth spreading across my stomach.

"Just Mila."

"Alright, Just Mila, that's what I'll call you."

I roll my eyes.

"Is there anything else?"

"I like it, too, when you use my whole name."

Now he breaks into a full-out grin, and I bite my lip to keep from smiling back. "Alright, Mila Kozak," he says as he runs his hands down my arms, making my skin tingle. "You got it."

I walk Cyrus and he finally poops, which literally brings me to tears. I've never been happier about poop in my whole life.

Alex brings two huge bags of tacos for everyone staying up at the barn—of course he does, because this is Alex we're talking about. Alex and I devour our tacos while standing in Cyrus's stall, our eyes never moving from Cy. The temperature has started to drop to a whopping 54 degrees, which in Florida certifies as Arctic. I've brushed and braided Cyrus's mane and tail, curried his gray coat until there's not one stray hair left, and picked his hooves clean. Now I just feel fidgety and cold. My Ukrainian ancestors are turning over in the frozen tundras of their grave as I shiver in subtropical Florida.

I'm snuggling up against Cyrus's chest for warmth when Alex returns with a sweater for me. I shrug it on and he offers to play music.

"It might help everyone calm down," he says, as if he needs a good reason to play music. "Anything you're in the mood for?"

I shake my head. He begins playing music from his phone, a song by Johnnyswim called "First Try." I stand at Cyrus's head, stroking his cheek, while Alex leans on the stall wall, tapping his foot.

"I love songs where the singers sing, like, over each other. I don't know what you call that," I say in reference to the chorus, when the duo are singing two different lines at the same time. "You'd think it would be too chaotic, but it's totally not."

"I've literally never thought about that."

"I love music."

"I can tell." He smiles at me, his eyes glimmering in the dark stall. "I love music too, but you've given me a new appreciation for it."

I raise an eyebrow at him. "How's that?"

He doesn't say anything for a moment, and then he holds out his hand and tucks me into his arms. "Maybe it has something to do with this," he says as he sways with me. "I haven't danced like this with anyone before."

I glance up at him, surprised. "You haven't danced with a girl before?"

He shakes his head. "I said I've never danced *like this* with a girl before. I've danced plenty, it's just, with you, it's different."

When the next song comes on, I look up at Alex only to find him gazing down at me, smiling.

"You have a perfect smile," he says.

"You have a really nice smile yourself, when you let yourself smile."

He laughs, close-mouthed, and says, "Well, my smile is far from perfect."

"Perfect doesn't equate to beautiful."

"No, but you're both."

His words are like a match striking within me, and suddenly all of my insides are on fire. Julia Michaels is singing about kissing in the cold, and I'm thinking Julia is really on to something. Our faces angle toward each other, our foreheads touching, when Dr. Canton breezes into the stall.

"Sorry to break up the party," he says as he quickly takes Cyrus's vitals. "He poop yet?"

Alex and I break apart, and I'm feeling flushed. "Yep, about an hour ago."

"Oh good." Dr. Canton stands up and looks at me, his eyes tired and drooping from a long night. "His vitals sound good, and his stomach sounds are returning to normal. I think we're in the clear."

I could weep from relief, except I'm too tired to muster any more tears. Dr. Canton squeezes me affectionately on the shoulder and slaps Alex's back as he gives us a few more instructions for the next few days and weeks for Cyrus.

By the time I feel comfortable leaving Cyrus's stall, the sun is peeking over the tree line behind the barn. My eyes are blurring and I can hardly walk in a straight line. It's a little pathetic that as a college student, I can't handle an all-nighter, but I prefer to think of it as a testament to my dad's strict upbringing that I never *had* to stay up all night to write a paper or study for a test. I just did it when I was supposed to. Either way, I'm not fit to drive.

"You okay?" Alex asks, and he puts a hand out as if he's going to catch me.

"Yeah." I rub my eyes. "I just might sleep in my car for a few hours before I drive home. I'm so out of it."

"Why don't you sleep upstairs instead?"

"Upstairs? Like, in your bed?" I meant to say, 'in your room' or even 'in your house,' but of course, because I'm me and this is Alex, it comes out as 'in your bed.' My cheeks warm as Alex looks at me, and I'm not going to lie, he looks frantic.

"My bed? Oh. Um…" He pauses, scratching the back of his neck. "I was thinking the couch? But my bed would be…fine. That would be fine. It's only, well, I won't be there." Now it's his turn to redden. "Uh, what I meant is that I won't be in the house, not the bed. I won't be in the bed. Not while you're there. Not, like that. It's just…" He groans and runs a hand over his face. I have to bite my lip to hold back a laugh. "It's been a very long night," he says from behind his hand.

I touch his arm and say, "The couch would be lovely."

"I have no qualms about you sleeping in my bed—it's only, well, it's my—"

"Alex," I cut him off, smiling as he flounders. "I'm totally great with the couch. Let's just get me there before I pass out."

"Right, yes. Let's."

Within moments of lying down on Alex's couch, I'm already dozing, only vaguely aware of Alex moving around the tiny barn apartment. I rouse as Alex carefully drapes a blanket on me, a gesture that feels endearingly intimate. And then, I sleep.

I'm in one of the deepest sleeps of my life, when I feel, even in my dreams, that someone is watching me. I open my eyes to find a slim older woman looking at me. And she is *not* happy.

"*Quien eres?*" she says, and I have no idea what she's saying, but it can't be good. "*Como llegaste aqui?*"

I sit up, patting my hair down, and say oh-so-eloquently, "Um?"

"*Donde esta Alex?*" And that one, I understand.

"He's downstairs, in the barn, I think," I say, finally finding my words. "He just let me sleep here because I stayed up all night with the horses—"

"*Quien eres?*" she repeats, and I realize she doesn't know what I'm saying, and I sure don't understand what she's saying. I realize at that moment that I'm still wearing Alex's sweatshirt, which I'm certain isn't helping the situation at all. I shirk the sweater off, and of course it pulls my shirt up with it, exposing my bra to this woman who I'm sure is Alex's mom. This really gets her going, and I just can't win here. I adjust my shirt and toss the sweater on the couch, determined to get out of here.

I stand up, and I'm skirting my way toward the door, when thankfully Alex walks in.

"Alex, *quien?*" she shouts, pointing at me.

I hold my hands up, like I'm innocent, though I don't feel it, the way she's looking at me.

"Mama, *calmate.*"

"*No me digas que me calme.*"

"Mama—"

At this point, I decide this is better for Alex and his mom to sort out amongst themselves, so I slip out the door and head down the stairs to wait for Alex. I don't have a toothbrush, and my mouth has that dry, sticky feeling of morning breath, so I find some water in the tack room and swish it around my mouth. I'm using my finger to scrub at my teeth when Alex walks in.

"I'm really sorry," he says, not even bothering to remark on my finger-brushing. "My mom got the wrong idea."

"It's a good thing we went with the couch."

He laughs and then asks, "You okay to drive?"

I nod. "Thanks for letting me sleep. Sorry I got you in trouble."

He smiles, and something tells me he feels like it was worth it.

The whole drive home, I'm dissecting my time with Alex. Every word, every look, every touch, it's all fresh in my mind. I'm pulling out moment after moment, examining it, and placing it carefully back where it belongs. At the forefront of my mind.

I think about when we were dancing to Julia Michaels' "Kissing in the Cold," when Dr. Canton walked in. And I'm imagining that he didn't walk in, that Alex actually did lean down and kiss me. I'm trying to think of what his lips would feel like on mine—warm, soft, inviting. I rub my knuckles over my own lips, and I realize I'm smiling as I think about him.

My phone is dead, so I can't play anything from my Spotify or else I'd play "Kissing in the Cold" a million times over. I turn on the radio. Every song is about Alex. From Post Malone's "I Like You" to Pink's "Never

Gonna Not Dance Again." Even a throwback by Kylie Minogue "Can't Get You Out of My Head" resonates with me. And that's when I realize, I'm in deeper than I realized.

I don't even remember that I never had Trina text Michael after I didn't show up to our dinner.

"Milochka!"

I'm finally home, and my mom is sobbing, pulling me into a wet hug. In the kitchen behind her, my dad is ashen-faced as he talks on the phone. My heart plummets and all of a sudden I'm thinking all of the worst thoughts—something happened to Anya, *Babusya* passed—but then my dad hangs up and he's hugging me too, saying, "I'm so glad you're safe, Milochka."

And now I'm completely bewildered.

"I just got off the phone with Trina," he says as he pulls away. "I finally got her to call me back after hours of trying. She said the horses were sick? That's why you didn't come home last night?"

I give them a guilty nod, realizing that my phone was dead the whole night and my parents had no idea what happened—they probably assumed the worst. "I'm sorry," I mumble, and I really feel terrible.

My dad seems relieved that I'm fine, but my mom is still crying, going on about, "First Anya, and then you. I thought my life was over."

My dad sighs, keeping his distance from my mom, and it makes my chest ache at the sight. He makes his excuses, saying he has to get back to work, and then my mom is just crying in my arms for what feels like forever while I stroke her hair and this time, I tell her it really is okay.

# Chapter Fifteen

# Untethered

I n the days since Cyrus's colic episode, I stay near the barn as much as I can. Michael—who was very understanding about the no-show when Cyrus colicked—has texted me a few times to try to reschedule our celebration dinner, but I keep putting him off for reasons I'm not willing to face yet. And, of course, he's being so understanding and chill about the whole thing that it's making me feel ashamed—*I* wanted this, and now that he's coming back to me, I'm almost ambivalent.

My funds are running low since I haven't gotten my applications in yet, so I approach Trina for help. I find her in her office, frowning over something she's writing.

"Oh." She looks up at me. "I'm glad you're here. I wanted to tell you about my conversation with the feed store."

I pull up a seat and lean my elbows on her desk.

"They said they had multiple reports of colic this week, so the issue was on their end. Although there's no excuse for us feeding the horses moldy feed. I can assure you we've had lengthy conversations with the staff about it."

"I appreciate that."

"I'm working up the chain of the manufacturing facility. I'm pushing for them to pay for the veterinary care we had to get for all of the horses."

I shrug because I'll be honest, as long as Cyrus is okay, I don't care too much about pointing fingers. Maybe I should; my dad would scold me for not being more litigious about this, but all that matters to me is that Cyrus is healthy.

"Thanks for following up on that."

"Of course."

I tap my fingers on the desk, trying to figure out how to segue out of this conversation, and just end up going for it. "Hey, so, what if I gave some lessons? Or, I don't know, help you flat some horses for your clients?"

Trina's eyebrows shoot up. "You want to teach lessons?"

"Um, yeah. Is that okay? I don't want to step on—"

"That's fantastic!" Trina jumps up and throws her arms around me in a rare display of affection. "Are you thinking you'd want to do this, like for real?"

"Um?"

"Instead of grad school?"

"Oh, I don't know..."

"You're going to *love* it, Mila. It's such a good fit for you."

"I guess we'll see."

Trina leans over her desk, looking at the schedule for the week. "How about you take the twins, Jasper, and Lena? Let's try that for this week. And I'll pay you for schooling Marina, Lily, and Holden's horses?"

"That sounds great."

"Perfect." And then she claps. Trina actually claps. Like a giddy schoolgirl. And I'm completely baffled.

Does everyone in the world have a better idea of what my future should look like than I do?

"Hey, I've been meaning to ask you," she says before I leave. "What's the latest with you and Alex?"

I give her a look that's trying to say, 'I have no idea what you're talking about.'

"Oh, don't give me that. I was there when you kissed him at the in-gate before your big ride."

"Oh, right," I say, fiddling with my belt loop. I had actually forgotten about that kiss with everything that happened after. "I thought I was going to die, Trina."

"Right, so if Carlos or Ryan or any other guy were at the gate at that moment, you would've kissed them?"

Shoot. She's got me. And she knows it, which means she's gloating. I slump down into the chair in front of her desk. "I don't know." I put my head in my hands.

"It doesn't have to be complicated, you know."

"It *is* complicated."

"Right, but I'm saying it doesn't have to be."

"If that's your guru advice for the day, I think I'm gonna go get started on flatting those horses for you."

Trina rolls her eyes and lifts both hands to shoo me from her office, but as I'm leaving she calls out, "Think about what I said, Mila."

I find that I do really enjoy teaching, especially the younger kids. It brings me back to a place of simplicity and pure joy. After a lesson with the twins, I'm in the barn tacking up a dun horse whose show name is Brooks & Dun, though around the barn we just call him Brooks.

"Hey," Alex calls out from the other end of the breezeway. "I have something for you. Don't go anywhere." And just like that, my heart is doing backflips while he disappears upstairs. I finish putting Brooks's bridle on and adjust the tack. I take my helmet off and smooth my hair because, let's be real, helmets aren't exactly the most flattering thing. I'm combing through my hair with my fingers when he comes back. He walks all the way up to me until he's only inches from me, which is the closest we've been since the night of Cyrus's colic, and I realize how badly I've missed him. I surprise myself by acknowledging it—at least, to myself.

"I've been thinking," Alex begins, and I inch almost imperceptibly closer to him. It feels like every cell in my body is yearning for me to get closer to him.

"Uh oh."

He nudges me playfully with his shoulder. "I've been thinking about what you want to do, you know, in the future."

"You've got it figured out, huh?" I want to tell him to get in line, but it's Alex, and I don't want to be rude.

He shakes his head. "No, no. But I thought you could figure it out." He hands me a beautiful leather journal with a strap wrapped around several times. I open it, and it's filled with blank pages, except for a note scrawled at the front, which says: "Mila, the sky is the limit.—Alex."

"I don't know what you'll do, Mila, but whatever it is, I know it'll be spectacular. And maybe writing down ideas, or just your thoughts, could help you figure it out. And, as an added bonus, I read that journaling before bed can help you sleep. So maybe it'll help in more ways than one."

"Wow." Tears prick at my eyes as I wrap the journal back up and hold it to my chest. And it hits me—there has never been, and probably never will be, someone as thoughtful. Someone who *gets* me the way Alex does. Whatever Michael and I had before, it can't hold a candle to what I'm forming with Alex. "Thank you, Alex."

He smiles a very self-satisfied smile and I can't help it, I have to kiss this guy. Maybe Trina was right and it doesn't have to be complicated. Everything is suddenly crystal clear as I look into Alex's endlessly deep eyes. "You're wel—" he starts to say, but I cut him off as I wrap my arms around his neck and press my lips against his. And, not for the first time, it feels like coming home. He smiles against my lips as he pulls me closer and deepens the kiss. The longer he kisses me, the more it feels like my cells are imploding from sheer happiness, like little bursts of fireworks going off all through my body.

"I guess you liked the gift," Alex says a moment later.

"I like you," I say, standing on tiptoes to kiss him again. "I *loved* the gift."

Alex chuckles. "At least we know where we stand." He holds out a hand in the air and says, "Me." Then he lifts his hand higher in the air. "Gift."

"Stop talking and just kiss me."

"Don't have to ask twice." He tangles his hands in my hair, lips moving against mine, when I remember that nothing is holding Brooks in place, and he just realized it, too. He starts clopping away down the breezeway, and Alex and I break apart to grab him. We're laughing as we chase the horse and catch him before he leaves the barn. I'm holding Brooks's reins, making sure he doesn't take off again, as Alex pulls me in for one last kiss. Which is, of course, the moment that Michael chooses to ride in on Khan.

Alex and I walk out with Brooks, and I try not to make eye contact with Michael even though I can feel his eyes boring into me as if I'd sprouted a second head. Alex gives me a boost into the saddle and I'm off on Brooks, feeling a wave of regret that I actually thought this could not be complicated.

As I trot Brooks around the ring, I think about all that Michael and I have been through—*two years* of memories—and yet it's strange that I suddenly feel so untethered from that. Like I'm floating through space, clipped to Michael, but Alex's gravity is tugging me away. It's shocking to realize that I *can* walk away from Michael. In a way, I still feel guilty because I was trying so hard to get back together with Michael. But now that I know I want Alex, it really is simple. I just have to unclip.

And, for the first time in weeks, I feel free.

Later, when I'm cleaning my tack, Michael walks in. I thought he'd left after his ride, so I'm surprised to see him. I was hoping for more time to collect my thoughts, to figure out what to say.

"Hey."

"Hey."

Silence stretches between us like a soap bubble about to burst. He's refusing to look at me, fidgeting with the strap of his helmet that he's holding.

"I, uh, just wanted to talk about"—I wave my hand in the general direction of the breezeway where Alex and I kissed—"what happened earlier."

"Okay?" I get the strange feeling like Michael *doesn't* want to talk about it, but I'm not going to do to him what he did to me. Leave things without a fair conclusion. We both need something to wrap up the relationship with. Not that it can ever be as neat and tidy as a bow, but still. We deserve this conversation.

I don't know how to say what I want to say, so I just blurt out the first thing that comes to my mind. "I've changed, Michael."

Michael tosses his helmet onto his tack trunk and shoves his hands in the pocket of his breeches. "Yeah but I thought the change was on a good trajectory—"

I shake my head. "I'm not the old Mila anymore." It's weird to admit this, and yet freeing at the same time. "And I won't ever be. And I think that means we're, just, y'know, not a good fit anymore." I think for a minute about how to say this next part, but there's just no good way. "But it doesn't mean I'm not a good fit for someone else."

"Okay?" Michael sighs. "You don't need my permission to date someone else, Mila."

I hold my chin up a bit higher, because in a way, he's right, I don't need his permission, and I'm just now realizing it. "I know."

"I am confused, though, because I thought we were kind of getting back together."

He steps closer to me, a flicker of hope in his blue eyes. His mouth is working, like he's trying to find the words to say, and for a moment I want him to say the right thing, I want him to fight for me.

"If you're worried about the long distance thing, we can work it out. I thought about it. You could apply to Vanderbilt, it's not that far—"

I put a hand on his arm, cutting him off. He did it. He said the right thing, but…it wasn't right enough for me. "Believe me, a few weeks ago, that's all I wanted. But now…"

"Yeah, yeah, I get it." He waves a hand dismissively. "The Cuban revs your engine or whatever."

"Michael!" I'm not even sure where to start with that. "His name is Alex."

"Yeah, okay," he mumbles, and a part of me wants to remind him that *he* broke up with *me* and he doesn't have a right to be upset. But then he looks at me with eyes that are painfully sad and says, "So, we're over? Just like that?"

Now it's my turn to sigh, my shoulders slumping. "Yeah, we are."

He steps closer to me, his hands hovering around my waist like he wants to hold me. "You sure that's what you want?"

"I'm positive," I say, and for the first time in a long time, I'm starting to feel confident in who I'm becoming.

He's glancing around the tack room, looking at everything *but* me, when he finally says, "Fine. Just, c'mere." He pulls me into a hug. I close my eyes and we hold each other for a few seconds. "I'm sorry, Mila."

And just like that, I realize, even though Michael is sorry, I'm not. Because all of this pain and heartache, it led me here—closer to the person I *want* to be.

I sigh, and lean into the hug a bit more. Michael puts his hand around my head, cradling me into him. And, I know in a way, Michael needs this—because I've battled it out in my head these past few weeks and have made my decision. He hasn't. Despite the intimacy of the hug, it's not romantic; it's a goodbye hug.

But that's not at all the way Alex sees it, as I open my eyes and realize that he's watching us from the doorway with a bridle hanging in either hand.

I yank away from Michael, feeling flush, my heart skittering around like an insect caught in my chest. Alex doesn't seem to know what to do as he lingers in the doorway, and neither do I. Eventually, he steps in, refusing to meet my eye as he puts the bridles roughly back on their hooks.

"Hey, man," Michael says casually, as if he's not aware of the tension in the room. Alex doesn't respond and leaves the tack room as quickly as he came.

"Alex—" I rush after him. "Hey, Alex." At first, he ignores me and doesn't turn around. I catch up to him, and tug at his arm. He pivots, but doesn't quite face me. "What you saw in there—it's not what you think. Like, at all."

"Yeah? And what exactly am I supposed to think?"

"I was just saying goodbye."

Alex shakes his head and says something to himself under his breath.

"I'm serious, Alex, it didn't mean anything."

He finally meets my eyes, and it's so devastating, I wish he hadn't. The swirling mess of agony I see there cuts me open. "It meant something to me, Mila."

"Are you talking about me hugging Michael? Or me kissing you?"

He raises both hands in the air. "All of it. The whole thing." Then, he gets out his phone, and I have no idea what he's doing but my heart is thudding so hard I can feel it all the way to my toes. "Maybe I could believe you about whatever was going on in there, if there wasn't this, too." And then he shoves his phone in my face, and there I am on Michael's Instagram account in my bathing suit.

My stomach bottoms out and I'm trying to find the words to explain all of this. I step closer to him, wanting more than anything to hold him, to reassure him. But as soon as I draw near, he backs away.

All of the closeness we'd had an hour ago is gone as the floor gives way and a chasm the size of the Grand Canyon yawns between us. *I can explain this, I can make this right,* I tell myself, but other than that, my brain is in shambles and an explanation isn't forthcoming.

"You're on Instagram?" And the minute the words are out of my mouth, I realize what it sounds like—like I got caught. But I'm honestly surprised Alex is on Instagram; for one, he's not following me, and two, he doesn't seem like the type.

I want to take back my question, take back the hug with Michael—at this point, I want to rewind the past few weeks and just choose Alex.

He shakes his head, his jaw clenching and unclenching. "Amber showed me."

I have a few thousand choice words for Amber as fury threatens to crack open my chest. Why is she ruining this? Why am *I* ruining it?

"Alex, please." I reach out a hand to him. "Can you just let me explain?"

"What is there to explain, Mila? I can see with my own eyes what's going on." He shrugs my hand off, and the gesture makes the fury in me take flight.

So I snap, "And what is it that you're seeing with those oh-so-perceptive eyes of yours?" I know it's the wrong thing to say, but I'm so pissed I can't think straight.

"That you're playing both sides of the fence."

"What? Of course I'm not doing that," I say, getting in his face, even though in the back of my mind, there's a voice saying, *he's right. You wanted to have your cake and eat it, too.* "I told you up front that I wasn't available, and yet you pushed—"

"Oh, this is *my* fault, is it? You didn't have to go out with me, Mila! I'm a grown man, I can accept a 'no'—which apparently you couldn't do with Michael."

It stings when he says it, like a slap to the face. Because he's right. I couldn't accept Michael's rejection of me. If I had, we wouldn't be here right now. The thought humbles me a bit, and I take a step back, lower my voice and say, "I don't even want to be with Michael anymore. Which, if you let me finish, you would know."

He's searching my eyes, looking for the truth in what I'm saying. There's a moment when I think he's going to give in and hear me out. He's going to forgive me and we're going to get through this. "I wish I could believe you."

I rake my fingers through my hair, desperate for something, anything, to get him to trust me. "What do you need me to say to convince you?"

"That's the thing. I never once wanted you to tell me what I wanted to hear. I always just wanted to know you. All of you—your hopes, your dreams, your fears, your nightmares. I've accepted all of that. But you, Mila, you refused to make that jump, to take that leap of faith, even though you knew I would catch you." His voice gets quiet, and it's absolutely desolating. "Why wasn't that enough for you?"

And before I can respond, he's gone. Just like that.

# Chapter Sixteen

# Sestra

It's been three days since Alex last spoke to me, and it's like I'm walking around with a gaping hole in my chest. It's laughable now that I ever thought I could walk away from him—but of course it's too late and I can't seem to convince him to give me a chance. Just when I was beginning to feel like a whole person again, it all implodes. And all of the pieces of me that were starting to mend have been scattered to the four winds and I'll never be able to recover them all.

I try to keep busy, but since I'm not competing with Cyrus for a couple weeks to let him recover fully after his colic, it's more challenging than usual. I spend most of my time teaching lessons, flatting horses for Trina, or making up for classwork I missed while I was taking care of Anya and then Cyrus.

One thing I haven't had the heart to do, though, is take the time to look at Natasha's feedback on my application essay. But when we have our monthly family dinner, my dad makes sure to bring it up.

Of course, the topic of conversation is usually all of the ways I'm not measuring up in my dad's sight, but this time around, I have Anya defending me.

"*Tato*, would you just let it go? She's a grown woman, she can manage herself."

"It's entirely evident to me that she can't. Seeing as how she hasn't gotten her applications in, Anochka."

"Did the deadline pass?"

"No," I say, the first word I've gotten in since my dad started his rant about responsibility fifteen minutes ago.

"See, Dad? It's fine."

My dad grumbles something under his breath in Ukrainian, but we all go back to silently eating our Pollo Tropical. Anya and I exchange a glance, both of us rolling our eyes in tandem. And, even though this family dinner is a pain in my butt, I am *so* glad to have Anya back on my side.

It *was* really nice to have Anya there after my fight with Alex the other night. "He'll come around, Milochka," she kept saying, though a couple days later, I'm still not sure, because all I've gotten from Alex is stony silence.

In fact, it feels like I'm getting that from *a lot* of people at the barn—including Amber. Which, I gotta tell you, is super confusing. Shouldn't she be happy I officially ended things with Michael?

Despite the silent treatment, I keep trying with Alex. And the whole time I'm wondering if I'm doomed to forever be desperately chasing one guy or another.

On a Wednesday afternoon, when I definitely should be in class, I'm sitting on the tack trunk in front of his apartment entrance when he finally comes out.

"Alex? Please, can you just hear me out?"

He exhales loudly, and I can see from the lines around his eyes that he's really tired.

"Fool me once, Mila," he says.

"How did I fool you, though? I've been honest with you this whole time."

"Maybe you think that's true, Mila, but I think the reality is that you haven't been honest with *yourself*. So how could you possibly be honest with me?"

And then, with that mic drop, he stomps up the stairs. I sit back down on the tack trunk, completely speechless. I tuck my knees up to my chest, remembering the night we spent curled up right here. That feels so far away right now, and I wonder if we'll ever get that back.

It's an overwhelming feeling that we might not ever be Alex-and-Mila. He *has* to listen to me, and if he won't hear me out in person, I realize I'll just have to write it down. I take my phone out and start writing a note to Alex, explaining everything. I don't know if he'll ever read it, but it's something. I *have* to tell him everything—where I was at when he first came into my life, and how he changed me. Even if he ultimately rejects me, he has to know what he means to me.

I'm still sitting there, twenty minutes later, typing furiously, when a cop car pulls up. I don't really think much of it, I'm too engrossed in what I'm doing, until the cops are pounding on Alex's door. Then I'm frozen to the tack trunk, wondering what in the world I should do.

Alex answers the door, and the police are saying something to him about allegations of poisoning the horses and not being a legal citizen, and suddenly Alex is in handcuffs and they're leading him to the car.

"Alex? What's going on?" I rush toward him, dropping my phone on the barn floor.

"I didn't do it, Mila." He looks back at me with so much fear, so much confusion and desperation, it brings tears to my eyes. "I don't know what they're talking about."

"You can't say anything without a lawyer there, okay?" I'm wracking my brain, trying to think of every police or legal show I've ever seen. But nothing could prepare me—or anyone—for this. "Don't sign anything. Don't say anything!"

But I don't know if he heard what I said as they shove him into the backseat of the cop car. His mom comes rushing down the stairs, and she's hysterical, speaking in Spanish so fast I can't catch anything she's saying. There's a moment when Alex's eyes flick over to his mom, and I see him through the window of the car as he closes his eyes and turns away. He doesn't want to watch his mom's reaction, and it's one of the most desolating moments of my life.

We watch the cop car drive away, and it feels like a piece of me is being ripped out and dragged away with Alex. I don't want to move. I don't want to breathe. I don't want to even think.

Beside me, his mom is quivering so much, I'm afraid she's going to have an epileptic episode. And, because there's no one else there to comfort her, I wrap my arm around her slender shoulder and say, "We're going to figure this out," even though I have no idea how.

She looks up at me with tear-rimmed eyes, her lips trembling, and shakes her head. We stand there, watching the police car turn out of the long barn driveway, and I wonder if she feels as paralyzed as I do.

A few of the other people at the barn walk out, and they're asking questions, but I just shake my head. I don't want to talk about it, especially with Alex's mom there. I'm about to bring her upstairs when I see Amber. And she is looking *smug*.

"What a pity, Mila," she says with absolutely zero pity in her voice. "Losing one boyfriend, then the other. I wonder who you'll steal next."

Her words strike me to my core, freezing me in place. "What are you talking about, Amber?"

She has the audacity to bat her long lashes at me like she's innocent. "It seems to me like you can land the guys, you just can't keep them. Too bad that one's illegal. And poisoning the horses? That's *next level*."

A rage I never knew I was capable of rips through me as Amber's words collide in my mind. And then, God help me, I pull back my arm and punch her.

After Amber is done cursing me out and threatening to call the cops on *me* now, I take Mrs. Caballero upstairs to her apartment and make her some tea. I don't even know if she likes tea, or if she wants to drink tea right now, but I also know that she has to stay as stress-free as possible because of her epilepsy. So tea seems like a really good idea.

Unfortunately, we can't communicate that well with each other. So mostly I end up pacing around her apartment, waiting for Alex to call, waiting for an idea. Anything. I call Trina about fifteen times, but I know she's in Naples for her niece's birthday.

I know for certain she's worried about Alex, but I wonder if she's worried about herself. If they deport Alex, will they deport her, too? I know Alex said he wouldn't mention his mom being here illegally if he ever got arrested, but how hard would it be for ICE to figure that out? Would it be better for Mrs. Caballero to be deported with Alex or to be here by herself with no one to take care of her? I'm not really sure.

Occasionally Alex's mom and I say something to each other in a language the other doesn't understand, but there's something about the interactions that seem to make us feel better, so we keep doing it.

"*Alex es un buen chico.*"

"He'll be okay, Mrs. Caballero."

"*No entiendo por que vinieron aqui.*"

"I'm going to figure out a way to fix this."

"*El va a estar bien.*"

A couple hours later, when Alex finally calls his mom from jail, I'm still there. She speaks to him first, in very rapid, very emotive Spanish. After a few minutes, she looks up at me and I gesture to her to say, *Can I talk with him?*

She must ask him, because I hear my name, though I don't understand the rest of what she's saying. She waits as Alex responds, and then, slowly, looks up at me with reticence. And shakes her head. He doesn't want to talk to me.

It feels like a slap to the face and suddenly my eyes are stinging with unshed tears. After Mrs. Caballero gets off the phone, I order her dinner via UberEats with the last few dollars in my bank account. I give her my number in case she needs something, but then I head home. No point in waiting around here anymore.

I'm dazed as I drive home—how did I get here? My conversation with Alex right before he was arrested comes back to me. He said I fooled him, but how? Because I wasn't 'honest' with myself? Is that true? I feel equal parts defensive and wholly ashamed. It's like my heart is on a roller coaster of emotions, going through the whole spectrum of every crappy feeling that ever existed.

Fear is like a fist clamping down on my whole life. And I'm so tired of it. I just don't know how to escape its hold.

I'm flipping through my Spotify account, trying to find a song that fits this moment, and I'm coming up short. I scroll and scroll, but nothing satisfies this moment where I want to rage, to cry, to get some answers. Every song feels hollow and disappointing. Music may be the doctor of the soul, but today, the physician is out. And I'm alone. Eventually, I turn off the radio and just listen to the wind rushing around my car as I speed down the Turnpike.

I call Trina again, but she doesn't pick up. I leave her a message telling her what happened with Alex. I'm not sure if she can do anything, but it's worth a shot.

At home, I grab my sneakers and head out for a run. To be clear: I am *not* a runner. But the fiery panic in my chest doesn't feel so disjointed when the rest of my body is burning too. I sprint down my street, and then, because of the aforementioned lack of running ability, I hobble down the next street. I'm fighting the crushing fear that I will always be alone, that I will always be rejected, that I will never be enough, that I will never know my own self enough to make anything of myself. When the dread builds, I start to sprint again, and I continue this way—sprinting, hobbling, sprinting—until my limbs are shaking and I can't distinguish whether my difficulty breathing is from a panic attack, or my unconditioned lungs.

I don't even have the energy to take my clothes off when I get back inside. I step into the shower fully clothed, except for my shoes, and sit there, my cheek against the cool tile until I stop quivering. After my shower, I debate whether to sleep in my room or Anya's, but decide to go to my sister's room. She's still awake, and my mom's downstairs drinking her nighttime tea, so Anya's watching a show by herself.

We both mumble sad greetings to each other—apparently Anya's mood matches mine. I curl into bed next to her and tell her, through tears, about everything with Alex. I wait for her words of wisdom, a grand idea, a way to smooth everything over and get Alex out of the clutches of deportation. But it never comes.

"I'm sorry, *sestra*," she says, because sometimes that's all you can say.

Eventually, Anya falls asleep and I drift off too, still feeling empty and alone because my sister can't even hug me.

I wake up in the middle of the night to Anya coughing. It takes me a few seconds to realize where I am, and who's coughing, but once it comes to me, I dart up.

"Anya?"

I can only see her dim outline in the dark room, but I hear something strange: a whistling sound coming from Anya's direction. Wheezing.

There's more coughing, and I'm not sure what to do, or where my mom is. I reach for my sister and prop her up as another coughing spasm wracks her body.

"Mom! Anya, it's going to be okay," I say, even though I definitely don't think it's going to be okay. "Mom!"

I hear a thud downstairs, and then someone's coming up the stairs. My mom bursts through the door and turns on the lights. There's a definite red spot on her forehead where she must have fallen asleep face down on the table again. She rushes to Anya's side, sitting her up more, and then she's fumbling in the bedside stand for her stethoscope. Her face is drawn and pale as she listens to my sister's lungs.

Anya has another coughing fit—a wet sounding cough that shakes me to my core—and then she spits something onto her blanket. My mom and I both look down to find red splattered on her comforter.

Blood.

"Mila, call 911," my mom says. "Right now."

My mom and Anya ride in the ambulance, and I'm following in my mom's SUV, my hands shaking the whole drive. Of course the parking lot is packed, and it takes me forever to find a spot, so by the time I find my mom, Anya is already getting a CT scan. I'm pacing the hallway, waiting for Anya to come back, and my mom isn't overly appreciative of my nerves, so she sends me to get something hot for both of us to drink.

"Maybe let's avoid any caffeine for you, hmm?" my mom suggests and I nod.

I find a Starbucks and get my mom a coffee and a chamomile tea for me.

When I get back, Anya has returned and the doctor is talking to them. He's throwing around words like *pulmonary embolism* and *thrombolytics* that I don't understand, but when he says, "We're admitting her right away and getting her into surgery," I get that. An involuntary shiver runs down my back, and I know that no amount of chamomile will get me to calm down.

Then, before I can even kiss my sister goodbye, they roll Anya away. I'm left with a hollowness in my gut, and then, surprisingly, bitterness. I realize, in a way, I'm mad at Anya. For being paralyzed—even though it's not her fault. For kissing Michael before we dated and not telling me about it. For being more needy than me for the first time in our lives. It suddenly makes sense to me why I've avoided Anya for so long, why I've struggled to be there for her. For a moment, I let the bitterness pool like acid in my stomach, dwelling there until it threatens to burn right through me.

And then, I let it go.

Like releasing a dove from my hands, the pain and bitterness flutters away and relief takes its place. I don't have to be angry anymore, or even fearful, and I find I don't want to be. Not when Anya's going into surgery, not when she might not make it through. I've used my anxiety as a wall, to keep my emotions in and everything else out, but I'm done with that.

I'm ready for New Mila. Even though I don't know exactly what that means, I want her. I want to let myself feel deeply, experience things fully, and not be so afraid of life.

I walk over to where my mom is sitting, drinking her coffee, and I take her hand. Squeeze it in mine. And tell her it's going to be okay.

I don't know how long it's been since Anya was admitted, but they got us a room with an armchair for my mom and one of the nurses brought in an extra chair for me. I keep nodding off, my head lazing from side to side, while we wait for Anya to return from surgery. They roll her in sometime after sunrise, and the sight of her brings tears to my eyes. She looks so fragile I don't even want to touch her.

But she's alive. I could weep with relief. And then, I do. My mom and I huddle together, holding each other and crying until we've shed all our tears. In a strange way, it feels good. Like I've let out something that would've turned to ash inside me if I hadn't.

An hour after Anya gets back from surgery, Trina calls me and I step out of the room to talk with her. She hasn't listened to my voicemail yet, and when I tell her what happened with Alex, she's stunned.

"Obviously someone accused him. The police wouldn't randomly show up," she's musing.

"I think it was Amber, she made some comments when Alex got arrested."

"Amber?" Trina's got some creative terminology to describe what she thinks of Amber.

"Can you do anything, Trina?" I ask, cutting her off.

"I'll try to track down where he is and I'll say whatever I need to say or sign whatever I need to sign to make sure they know he didn't poison the horses. I'll get someone from the feedstore and the vet to send something in, too."

"Thanks, Trin."

"Don't thank me yet," she says grimly. And then I tell her about Anya. I'm openly weeping in the hallway on the phone, but I don't care. I don't want to burden Trina with any more bad news, but also, she's my friend. And friends deserve to know the good *and* the bad in my life—they can't know how to help me if I don't tell them in the first place.

"I'm so sorry, Mila."

I take a page from Alex's book. I don't say, *It's okay*. I just say, "Thank you." Because I *am* grateful for Trina's empathy. She doesn't have to solve my problems for me; just feeling with me is enough for me right now.

We chat for a few more minutes and then hang up. My dad shows up about twenty minutes later, and we're all standing around Anya's bed, watching her sleep, and I can't shake the image of Anya in a casket.

*She's alive*, I keep telling myself. I glance from Anya's face to her vital signs monitor, watching her heartbeat blip steadily. After long minutes of standing that way, it's decided that I'll go get breakfast for everyone. I leave the room feeling like I'm deserting a part of myself—it's not like we're going to eat, anyway. I know my parents just want to talk without me there.

It's strange how the hierarchy in our family got messed up after Anya's accident. My parents always told Anya what was going on, and she would deliver that information to me in her authoritative, firstborn kid kind of way. But now, they tiptoe around both of us like we're both crippled. And it sucks.

While I'm trying to find my way to the cafeteria, I see a sign for the chapel and I follow it. The door to the chapel is made of stained glass panels, but once I step inside, it's just a normal room, except for the very morbid painting of Jesus at the front of the room. It's like no one thought about the fact that someone mourning or praying for their family members might not want to see that. What about Jesus with some sheep? Or some kids? That seems more comforting.

I walk cautiously to the front of the room, which is filled with short pews and a table at the front with various Bibles and some fake candles. When I get to the first pew, I stop short, because there's a man on the ground. He's kneeling, and now that I'm close, I can hear him sniffling, his broad back quivering as he cries. The sight cuts me sharp, and I back away as quietly as I can. And, as I leave the chapel, I pray that that won't be me anytime soon.

I return with a very questionable breakfast of rubbery eggs, too-shiny sausage and brick-like toast. Anya's still asleep, so we all push our food around silently, without actually eating. Eventually, the only choice for conversation is, of course, my applications.

"You get them in?" my dad asks.

I shake my head.

"Well, sweetheart, if you need a distraction, you could go work on those," my mom says, and I shoot her a look that says, *Not you, too, Mom.*

"I want to wait for Anya to wake up." And then, because I can't handle sitting here in silence or listening to my parents badger me about applications, I pull out my AirPods. But every song I listen to reminds me of Anya or Alex in some way and brings a fresh wave of crippling despair.

It's like I'm caught again in a rip current of fear—the waves are crashing over me, threatening to pull me under. I can't get enough air; my chest is tightening and it takes all of my self-control to not tear at my shirt so I can get a full breath. Everything feels distorted, like up is down and down is up. I have no idea how to get out of this. What if I lose Anya just when I finally got her back? What if I lose Alex, not just as my boyfriend, but as my *anything.* Gone, to Cuba, where who knows what will happen to him. His whole life here, abandoned. His dreams, vacated. And his mom. Fear for her worms its way into my mind until I'm struggling to juggle all of these people I'm worried about.

So much for *New Mila*, I think bitterly.

I end up playing a random podcast by Malcolm Gladwell about Mc-Donalds french fries. I can't possibly pay attention to it right now, but it keeps me in my own bubble, fortunately distant from my parents and *almost* distracted from my anxiety.

An hour later, Anya starts to stir, and my mom calls a nurse. We all stare at her, watching every breath, every eye flutter.

"Anochka," my mom says, stroking my sister's hair. My dad's at her feet, squeezing them. I'm on the opposite side of the bed from my parents and I take Anya's hand in both of mine.

We move aside as the nurse, a petite Black woman in neon green Nikes, comes to check on Anya. She adjusts the cannula in my sister's nose and listens to her lungs.

"Sounds much better in there," the nurse says, smiling. "Dr. Talan will be doing rounds in about an hour. Can I get you anything? Some juice?"

She brings us little containers of juice and packages of graham crackers. I grab the cranberry juice, but it's way too sugary and somehow still too tart, and my taste buds tingle as I sip it. We eat the graham crackers, probably because our breakfast was too horrible to eat, and now that Anya's kind-of-sort-of conscious, our fears are slowly losing their vice grips on our stomachs.

As I'm finishing my second pack of graham crackers, Anya wakes enough to say she's thirsty. My parents sit her up and give her a few sips of juice while I watch helplessly. It's in this moment that I realize how much of a third wheel I am in Anya's healthcare. I wish I knew what to do, how to help, but I often feel like I'm on the outside looking in. I flash back to the days after her accident, when I sat in the corner of her hospital room just like this.

I'm so tired of this. And yet, I don't know how to change it. I even go so far as to discreetly Google on my phone, "course for quadriplegic caretakers," and I save a few of the options that pop up.

My parents are whispering to each other in Ukrainian when Dr. Talan walks in, and despite the gloominess circulating in the room, he's smiling underneath his bristling mustache. "Anya...Anya Kozak?" He's looking at her chart, and then he says, in Ukrainian, "*Ti Ukrainitz?*"

"*Tak z Kharkova,*" my dad says, his eyes wide. It's not often you run into another Ukrainian. They laugh, and we all shake his hand as if we just found out he was a long lost uncle of ours.

This breaks all the tension in the room, and even Anya's smiling weakly, as Dr. Talan examines her thoroughly. "Now, young lady," he says once he's finished. "We have to find a way to get you moving."

"No offense, doc"—my sister blushes, her pale face brightening—"but I'm, uh, paralyzed."

He chuckles. "I know, but your blood clot, along with all of the bedsores I'm seeing, tell me that you are not moving enough. It looks like you didn't finish your physical therapy. Have you been doing your passive range of motion exercises?"

Anya shakes her head. Her face is frigid, and Mom looks chastened. Looking between them, I can tell that this is a point of tension between them. Has Anya not wanted Mom to do her exercises for her? And why in the world did she not finish physical therapy? I shake my head; none of this makes sense.

"Why is that?" Dr. Talan asks, sitting on the edge of her bed.

Anya tilts her head back and closes her eyes, tears spilling out. We all gather around her bed, touching various parts of her body as we all attempt to comfort her.

"I don't want this," Anya finally says. "I didn't ask for this. I don't want this life, where someone has to do everything for me. Where I'm the sick one, the needy one."

"Oh, Anochka," my mom cries, and even my dad is blinking back tears.

Dr. Talan sighs and squeezes Anya's shoulder. "Depression is normal after a life-altering accident like yours. I have some recommendations, when you're ready for them."

Anya nods her head, pressing her lips together to try to keep from crying, but the sob escapes anyway. We're all clutching at Anya, and it's the saddest thing because even though we're all holding on to her, she can't feel it.

And it breaks my heart.

After Dr. Talan leaves, I give my parents and Anya some time to talk. I'm walking aimlessly around the hospital, despairing for Anya, despairing for Alex, and, sadly, most of all, despairing for myself. Just a week ago, I felt like I had everything—I finally felt closure with Michael, I was confident enough to compete in a Grand Prix with Cyrus, I had reconciled with Anya, and was falling for Alex.

But now all of that was taken from me—or maybe I never had it in the first place. Anya's still just a shell of herself, refusing help, refusing to move forward in her new life. Alex is gone, maybe forever. I still have Cyrus, but even that feels bittersweet right now. A sob is forming in my throat, and I choke it down.

I wander down one hall until I see a train of patients in wheelchairs being pushed into a room. Most of them have bald heads, so I assume they're here for chemo or radiation, but as I walk closer, I see a sign on the door they're entering: Cancer Support Group.

At first, I don't think anything of it, but when I peek into the room, and see all of their wheelchairs gathered in a circle, it gets me thinking. And suddenly I'm remembering the notebook Alex gave me right before everything went to crap with him. I don't have the journal on me right now, so I open the notes app on my phone, and I write.

I write my hopes, my dreams, my ideas—despite all that's been taken away from me, or perhaps *because* of everything that's been taken from me. I write. I write for Anya, for Alex, for myself. For the person I am now and the one I want to become. Because change is not a linear thing, it goes up and down like a stock market graph. Some days I'll be Old

Mila, some days I'll be New, but every day I'll get closer to the person I want to be.

And for the first time in days, there's a tiny bit of hope ballooning in my chest. It's so fragile, I fear it'll burst with a wrong move, but it's there. And right now, a little bit of hope is all I need.

Once I finish the note, I remember there's one other note I need to complete. I go back to my message to Alex, add a few more sentences, then copy and paste it into my text thread with him. I don't know if he'll be able to see it right now, but whenever he does see it, he'll know how I feel. And right now, that's the best I can hope for.

When I get back to Anya's room, I ask my parents if I can talk with Anya by myself. My mom nods and leaves the room, but my dad of course has to make a comment: "Fine, Milochka, but after your chat, I want you to finish your applications."

I want to say, *Really, Dad? Right now?* But instead I ignore him and he walks out, already on his phone. I sit on Anya's bed and stroke my fingers through her hair.

"Are you going to lecture me, too?" Anya asks.

I shake my head. "Maybe another day." And I give her a small smile to tell her I'm kidding.

She rolls her eyes, but I can tell there's less tension in her face as she says, "Thank the heavens."

"I just wanted to tell you one thing, though."

She cocks an eyebrow at me like, *Didn't you just say you weren't going to lecture me?*

"It's not a lecture. It's something I think you need to hear."
She sighs.

"I need you, Anya." I look into her eyes so she can see the pain, the heartache, and the hope in them. All of the bitterness, though, is gone. "I need you so much, even if you're paralyzed, even if you can't walk, I need you."

My sister's blinking back tears, and then I am, too. I take her hand and hold it up to my cheek so that when the tears drip down, she catches them.

"This past year has been a nightmare. I've been so alone, fumbling through my life without you. And I know you feel like you want to give up and stop living and not be dependent on people, but guess what? I'm depending on you. I need you to keep living so that I can keep coming to you with all my problems. Because, guess what? I got a lot of problems."

She laughs then, even through the tears, because she knows it's true.

"So, please, *sestra*, don't give up." And then all the emotion from the past twenty-four hours is choking me so that I can barely make out the words. "I need you."

And then we're full-on ugly sobbing, because apparently that's what we do together these days, and I'm holding her and in her own way, she's holding me, too.

After Anya and I have cried ourselves senseless, I gather my things and I've decided I'm finally going to get my applications in. Because what else do I have to lose? As I'm getting ready to leave, Anya says, "You shouldn't let him bully you."

"And my choices are...?"

Anya does her eye-shrug, and then says, "Not apply for grad school if you don't *want* to go to grad school?" as if this is actually an option.

I laugh glumly, but Anya presses the issue.

"I'm serious, Mila. If you don't want to go, don't go."

"I don't know what I want," I say, even though that's not totally true anymore. Something is taking shape in my mind, but I don't have the courage to say anything about it. Not yet. Besides, my dad being happy with me *is* something I want, very much.

Before I leave the room, Anya says, "Just because *Tato* is a bulldozer doesn't mean you can't be one, too."

And *this* is why I need Anya so much. Because she says stuff like that right when I need it. Immediately, an idea forms and I scramble over to kiss Anya. "Thank you, thank you, thank you."

"For what?"

"I gotta go."

"What are you going to do?" she calls out as I'm in the hallway. I stick my head back in her room and smile at her.

"I'm gonna bulldoze."

# Chapter Seventeen

# Bulldozers Gonna Bulldoze

I find my parents in Starbucks. They're at the same table, but they're both staring at their phones, facing away from each other. It's a sad sight, but not one I can deal with right now.

"Hey, Dad, can I talk to you for a minute?"

They glance up at me, seeming relieved to have a reason to depart from each other.

"I'll go back up to Anya," my mom says, excusing herself.

"Sure," he says, but he's still typing a message on his phone. I wait for him to put his phone down, and it takes longer than I think it will. I'm literally tapping my foot impatiently until he glances up at me. "What did you want to talk with me about?"

"Remember my friend Alex?" And, of course, he doesn't, so I remind him about Alex's predicament.

"Milochka, I already told you, I'm too—"

"Dad." I level my gaze at him. "Do you want me to apply to grad school?"

My hands are shaking, and I put them flat on the table to keep my nerves from showing.

*I am a bulldozer. I am a bulldozer,* I tell myself.

"What does that have to do—"

"Answer the question, *Tato.*"

"Yes, Mila, it's the only thing I've wanted you to do for months now."

I don't bite at this particular fallacy. I just don't have time, and neither does Alex.

"Look, if you want me to apply, you will help Alex."

My dad is silent for a long time, his hazel eyes squinting at me.

"What are you saying, Mila?"

"I'm saying, if you help Alex, I will get my applications in tonight."

He leans back in his seat, tapping the table with his fingers. "And if I don't?"

"I won't apply."

"You can't be serious—"

"I am more serious about this than anything I've ever been serious about in my life."

Another silence. His eyes darken as he examines me to see if I'm serious. Then he bursts out laughing. As in, real, guttural laughter that has him wiping his eyes. He gets out of his seat and pulls me into a hug, and I am baffled. Is my dad *mocking* me?

"Oh, Milochka," he says, still chuckling. "I am proud of you, my sweetheart."

"Um?" I say confidently. Because, I am a bulldozer. *Right?*

"Excellent negotiation tactics. You're obviously learning something from that overpriced university."

"Uh…" I almost tell him he could've saved his money and just sent me to Anya, but I let him think it's UM that taught me this whole bulldozer thing.

"I'll help your friend. But I want to see a finished essay before that."

"Deal."

And my dad actually extends a hand to shake on it. We shake, and I fly to the library faster than Cyrus in a speed class.

The next day, I'm in the library with Monica, *finally* turning in my grad school applications when I get a call from my dad's lawyer. I rush out of the study room like I'm on fire and fumble to answer the call.

"Hello?"

"Mila? This is Ann, I'm your dad's attorney."

"Yes, yes, hi, Ann. Thanks for calling me."

"I just wanted to let you know, Alex is going to be released in about an hour."

"Oh! Oh wow, thank you, Ann, oh my gosh. Can you, um, send me the address?"

"Texting it to you right now."

"Thank you so much."

"My pleasure. Have a good one."

We hang up, and with shaking hands, I tell Monica what's going on, then text Anya an update—which means my mom knows now, too. I call my dad, but it goes to voicemail. I leave him a quick message, and then practically run to my car, my heart racing the whole way up to the Broward Transitional Center, where Alex is getting released.

When I pull up to the Center, I show my ID to the guard at the gate and pull into the parking lot. I immediately recognize my dad's matte black Tesla and a thrill runs through me that my dad is actually helping me, helping Alex.

As I hurry toward the massive pink building, I have a moment where I hesitate. What if Alex isn't happy to see me? What if he's still mad at me? I don't *think* he's had access to his phone while in custody, so there's a good chance he hasn't read my message yet. I slow to a walk, my stomach dropping as I open the front door.

There, in the foyer, is my dad, a woman I presume is Ann the lawyer, and Alex. The second Alex's eyes meet mine, I know.

Without even caring that my dad and his lawyer are right there, I catapult myself into Alex's arms, and—thank God—he catches me. I burrow my head into his neck, and he smells of cheap soap and sweat, but it's the best smell in the world to me right now. He holds me against him, and I never want him to let go, except that my *dad* and his lawyer are standing right behind us. So, even though it hurts, I step away from Alex.

I shake Ann's hand and give my dad a kiss on the cheek and together we walk toward our cars. Ann and my dad seem to sense that Alex and I want to be alone, so they say their goodbyes.

Then Alex and I are in the middle of the parking lot, holding each other. I hug him closer, wanting every part of me to be touching every part of him. He leans in, putting his head on my forehead.

"Thank you," he says. "You didn't have to do all of this for me—"

I back away, hands on my hips, as I tell him, "Yes, I did, Alex. I don't want to lose you. I just found you."

"Can I tell you something?" he says, pulling me close to him so that when he talks, I can feel his breath against my lips. "You've had me for a long time."

My mouth tips cautiously into a smile. "What do you mean?"

He runs a finger along my jawline. "Maybe one day I'll tell you." Then he stands back and his shoulders sag. "I'm sorry I wasn't willing to hear you out about Michael. The whole thing really threw me for a loop, and with those pictures he posted, I just thought…"

"I know what you thought, but I think Michael was doing that on purpose. He's not a bad guy, but I think he was trying to mark his territory."

"I can see that now." He sighs and rubs a hand across his face. I can tell he's worn out, and I can't even imagine what he's been through these past few days. What even happens inside those facilities? "One of my roommates, this guy Manny, he kind of helped me reason it out."

"Sounds like a smart guy."

"He also offered to get me a U.S. birth certificate off a dead guy for fifty grand."

"So he's an outside-the-box thinker."

He shakes his head, but he's smiling at me and my insides feel like they're melting. He reaches out a hand and reels me in. "I read your text."

"Yeah?" I wrap my arms around the back of his neck, tugging him closer. "I didn't know if you'd have your phone."

"Oh, I didn't. I literally just read it in the bathroom right after they gave me back my stuff."

I have so many questions about his experience—was it like jail? Did he have guards? Did they cuff him? Were there gangs? But all of those questions will have to wait because right now, I just want to know, "What did you think?"

"I think"—his mouth tilts up at one side—"that I want to kiss you."

I laugh and say, "I've been waiting a long time for *you* to kiss *me*."

He pulls me tight against his chest and lowers his mouth to mine. And there has never been—and maybe never will be—a kiss sweeter than his. It's long and slow, a lingering kiss that stays with me even after our lips have separated.

I burrow into him, reveling in the feel of his arms around me, enveloping me, so that I can't tell where I end and he begins. We stand like this for what seems like a few minutes, though I'd be okay if it were an eternity.

"So"—I cock my head to the side so I can see his face—"why did they release you?"

Alex leans back, not quite separating us, but creating enough distance so that I can see his expression. He's smiling playfully, but his eyes are hazy with an emotion I can't quite identify. "Here I thought you *wanted* me out."

I give him a flirtatious push to his chest, enjoying the feel of him underneath my palms. "Of course I wanted you out. I'm just surprised Ann got it done so quickly."

"Well, as soon as the police talked to Trina, they dropped the poisoning charges against me. Trina got Dr. Canton to submit an affidavit saying that the cause of the colic in the horses was moldy feed—it was an accident, not intentional. They tested the feed and everything."

"No one with half a brain would actually think you poisoned the horses."

"Yeah but the cops didn't know that; they're not horse people. For all they know, horse poisoning is rampant amongst show jumpers."

"I mean, who's to say you're not the next Tommy Burns," I say, referring to an infamous horse killer who was contracted by owners wanting to collect on high-ticket insurance policies on their horses.

Alex rolls his eyes but I laugh to myself, because there couldn't be a person out there more juxtaposed than Alex and *any* horse killer. I'd laugh harder if we were farther from the Broward Transitional Center.

"I'm glad Trina and the vet stuck up for you."

"Me too."

"So what about deportation? Is that, y'know, on the table?" I almost don't want to ask the question, because I can't handle the answer if it's yes.

"I have to go to court, but Ann says the system's so backed up, it might be a year or two before I'm in front of a judge. She says I have a good chance of staying here, since I have a clean record, I'm in school, and I've been here since I was a kid."

I breathe a huge sigh of relief and tangle my fingers with his, squeezing his hand tight.

"Your dad paid my bail."

I look up at him, surprised. "Really?" I honestly didn't know ICE detainees needed to post bail, but I'm grateful my dad was willing to help, and even though I did bully him into it, it seems like he went above and beyond for me.

He nods, smiling down at me, and I hug him again. Then I tell him about my bulldozer tactics with my dad.

"Whoa, look at you, boss."

I make a face at him when he calls me boss, but then I say, "You can call me that just this once, because right now, I *am* a boss."

"Agreed."

I stand on tip-toe and plant a soft, quick kiss on his lips. "Alex?"

"Yeah?"

"I choose you."

His lips quirk into that perfect half-smile of his that makes me feel shaky inside, and he cups my chin and brings my lips to his again.

"And I choose you, Mila Kozak."

I smile, feeling tingly and happy as I run my fingers through his hair. "I like when you call me that."

"I'm a good listener," he says, smiling. "Mila Kozak." And I kiss him again.

I drive Alex back to the barn. When we get there, there's a truck and horse trailer in the driveway that I don't recognize. But then, Alex's mom is running out of the barn, holding her arms out to her son, and it brings tears to my eyes. She's hugging him, crying, and then she reaches up and puts both hands on his face.

"*Mi hijo*," she says, rubbing her thumbs across his cheeks, "*estoy tan feliz de que estés aquí.*"

"*Yo también*, mama," he says, and kisses her cheek. I think she'll probably never let go of Alex—and let's be real, I didn't want to either—but finally she releases him and walks over to me. I'm not exactly sure where we stand, considering our first interaction and the fact that I still don't understand most of what she's trying to communicate to me. I hope she appreciated that I stuck around with her after Alex was arrested, but I can't be sure.

She takes both of my hands in hers and says, "Thank you," and a smile breaks out across her face, the wrinkles around her eyes puckering, and I see where Alex gets his smile from.

I smile back at her and say, "*De nada.*"

This makes her laugh, and she turns to Alex, giving him a thumbs up and says, "*Ella me gusta.*"

"*Yo tambien*, mama," Alex says, his eyes dancing as he looks from his mom to me. Together, we walk toward the barn when Amber comes striding out, holding her horse, Zippo, by the leadrope. She brushes past us, refusing to make eye contact, and walks her gelding into the waiting trailer. Trina's right behind her, looking smug.

"Don't let the door hit you on the way out," she says to Amber, who doesn't turn around. She gets into the passenger seat of the truck and gives me an absolutely frigid look.

"She's lucky you're not pressing charges," Trina says to Alex.

I glance up at him and ask, "Is that true? You're not going to press charges against her for lying about you like that?"

"I don't need retribution." Then he looks at me and he's smiling down at me and it's making me feel like something in my chest just sprouted wings. "I've got everything I need."

That night, when I get home, I find my mom sitting at the kitchen table, asleep. Anya's back home, her monitor on the table right in front of my mom. She stirs when I walk in and check the monitor. Looks like Anya's asleep, too.

"Milochka," she says, rubbing her eyes.

I make her some tea, since that just seems like the right move these days, and decide I could use some, too. I use a minty loose leaf tea someone gifted my dad for Christmas, and dump honey into it. Because that's the only way to drink tea.

My mom sips hers gratefully, and we sit in silence for a while. That's the nice thing about my mom—or maybe it's just a moms-in-general thing, I'm not sure—I don't have to say anything with her, I can just be.

But there is something I want to say to her.

"You're a really good mom."

She startles at my words, blinking at me over her teacup, and it makes me laugh.

"Apparently I need to tell you that more often."

She reaches across the table and takes my hand in hers. Compared to my calloused rider's hands, my mom's hands are smooth and almost papery. "I'm just a little...surprised. That's all. I've been very consumed with your sister. Honestly, I've missed you, Mila."

"I know. Me too. But you needed to take care of Anya, and I get that. Even though I have felt the loss of that."

We both sip our tea, lost in our own thoughts. Eventually, I add, "I know that Anya needs you, and I know you have your hands full, but I also want to make sure that you don't lose your life to Anya's."

A small smile plays on my mom's lips. "That's motherhood, sweetheart."

"I just don't think Anya would want that for you. I, for one, don't want that for you. And I know Dad doesn't either."

"Your father has been very clear about what he wants and doesn't want."

"Maybe he doesn't really know, and he's running away from the decision," I say, because that's my move, and I know who I got it from. And it's definitely not from my mom, who throws herself head-first into any problem.

"I'll think about it," she says. I kiss my mom goodnight and head upstairs, where I peek into Anya's room and give her a kiss as well.

Once I'm in bed, I pull out the notebook Alex gave me, running my fingers over his inscription. Then I grab a pen, and start to write.

# Chapter Eighteen

# Symphony No. 5

I t's the last Sunday of WEF. It's the biggest Grand Prix of the season—the CSI Five-Star Lugano Diamonds Grand Prix, with a $500,000 pot, which means the winner will get about half of that. I'm waiting at the in-gate, with Trina on my right and Alex on my left. I can't say that I feel zen—not even close—and I did my obligatory pre-Grand Prix heaving in the barn before I rode out here. But I'm here.

Along the edge of the stadium, seated at a ringside table at the International Club are my parents, Anya, and Monica. Heidi, the owner of Zen Elite Stables, offered up her table when she found out that Anya and my parents were coming to watch the Grand Prix. Anya looks like a movie star, with her cat-eye Gucci sunglasses and her hair blowing gently around her face. Today when I look at her, I don't feel sad. I just feel grateful—grateful she's alive, grateful she's my sister, and grateful for all we've been through together.

Laura Kraut is on her course and, can I just say how surreal it is that I'm going on course after Olympic gold medalist Laura freaking Kraut? Laura finishes the course, clean, and I take a deep breath.

"Good luck, chica," Trina says as she pats Cyrus's rump.

Before I go in the ring, I lean down, grab hold of Alex's shirt, and kiss him. It's my good luck charm, and I never go into the ring without it.

I heel Cyrus into a canter and we make a loop around the water jump. It feels like I'm a conductor, tapping her baton to ready my player—Cyrus. He dances beneath me like a violinist setting their bow on the string. Waiting with bated breath for me to raise my hand to start the symphony.

The announcer's voice warbles over the speakers, the buzzer sounds and the symphony begins.

As we gallop toward the first jump on course, Cyrus's hooves pound out a staccato on the arena floor. The sound hits a crescendo until suddenly, it stops. We're soaring over the white Lugano Diamonds oxer, a Grand Pause as we seem to hang in the air for several long seconds.

We fly to the next jump, Cyrus in full animato as the music of our ride pushes us on through the course. Once he sees the liverpool with the huge lighthouse standards, he side-steps nervously. I press my heels into his sides and click at him to keep going. He gives an almighty leap that has me clutching my legs to the saddle so as not to go flying. The landing is a shock to my knees, a missed note on the strings. We re-group, making a wide turn toward the next line.

I collect my reins, sitting back in the saddle as I attempt to control my runaway orchestra. It only takes a moment, and we're back in tandem as we skyrocket over the black-and-gold CDD Wealth Swedish oxer.

Next is an in-and-out with two delicate verticals. Cyrus gives them plenty of room and then we're charging toward the biggest oxer on the course—the other Lugano Diamonds jump. We race at the obstacle, a lively allegro as we approach the jump. He launches us over and I'm lifting my maestro hands up and over, as if I can carry him over this gargantuan jump. It feels like we're in the air for minutes, not seconds, before we're making a tight turn to a long line. Cyrus's feet are pounding over the ground and the wind is adding its own notes to our song. But Cyrus and I are in perfect harmony as we symphonize through the course. I can't think of anything but the jump in front of us, Cyrus beneath me and this beautiful canticle we're creating.

We are notes on a page come to life; sweeping, soaring, up and over until we reach the heavens.

Jump after jump, it seems like all of the stadium has joined our chamber—Cyrus's feet, the percussion, the reins in my hands, the strings, the wind in our faces, the woodwinds, each jump a member of the brass. It's a production that won't soon be forgotten.

And then, we're approaching the last combination, a triple—two oxers with a precarious vertical right in the middle. This is our spiccato, Cyrus's hooves barely touching the ground in between the jumps. Our cadence is flawless; one stride to the vertical, and then two more strides to the next oxer, all in perfect tempo, like this is what we were made to do. We were made to sing this song.

The very last jump in our symphony is the sprawling water jump with a row of flower boxes in front of it. He lets loose, his powerful hooves performing his loudest fortissimo. I urge him on, and then we're flying up, up, up. Cyrus sprouts wings as our melody glides over the water.

Then, we're through the timers. The crowd is cheering, a standing ovation, because we are clean.

This is our aria, our opus dedicated to the love of air-time.

"That's a clear round, ladies and gentlemen, for Cyrus Van der Bergh and Miss Mila Kozak of Miami, Florida, with a time of 78.48," the announcer croons. "We'll be seeing this pair back for the jump off."

I lean down and throw my arms around Cyrus's neck. He's tossing his head and I know he wants the reins, so I give it to him and look up to find my family. Monica is waving her hands in the air, shouting something I can't quite hear. Anya is screaming a triumphant, "Woo! Woo!" and my mom and dad are both standing, clapping and smiling. And then, they hug each other, which makes mine and Anya's eyes widen, because I don't think they've touched—not in a positive way, anyway—in a long time.

And then Rodrigo Pessoa is passing me on his way into the arena, and I'm craning my neck around because, did Rodrigo Pessoa just pass me? Am I dreaming? But sure enough, there's another Olympian I'm competing against and the thrill is too much to contain.

Back in the schooling area, I jump off of Cyrus and both Alex and Trina tackle me into a group hug. Trina's slapping the top of my helmet and chanting, "We're going to the jump off, we're going to the jump off," and Alex has the biggest smile that I've ever seen him wear. He kisses me and then takes Cyrus's reins from me.

"I'll walk him around to keep him warm until the jump off." I watch as two of the most important guys in my life walk away, and then Trina's grabbing my elbow, pulling me back toward the ring.

"Let's talk before you get too moony-eyed."

I laugh and let her tug me away so we can talk through the course and make plans for the jump off.

I'm last in the jump off since I had the fastest time in the first round, which is epically unreal.

"Our last rider on course today, Miss Mila Kozak and Cyrus Van der Bergh," the announcer says, and begins chattering on about Cyrus's age and that this is our first season competing together and so on. It occurs to me then, no one talks about how tough it is to break into the horse show announcer's racket if you're not a British male.

I can't dwell on the injustice of it, though, as I walk Cyrus up to the lighthouse jump—the one he balked at in the first round—and let him have a closer look. He points his ears sideways at it and does a very prim snort.

"It's okay, Cy," I tell him, but he doesn't seem convinced.

And then the buzzer chimes and we're on course. First the Lugano oxer, then we're attacking the lighthouse jump. This time I have Cyrus firmly in hand, legs wrapped around his sides, urging him on. He rabbit-hops over the fence, but somehow clears it.

I'm spinning him on his hind end and we're over a plank fence and then we're galloping to the enormous Lugano jump, sprawling over it in the purest form of flying ever experienced.

Every cell in my body is focused on getting Cyrus over these jumps. This is what Trina's been trying to convince me of this whole time—there is no remembering here, we are just living. Immersed in what's right in front of me, fully present because I have no other choice.

We're jumping the skinny wave jump in the reverse direction from the first course, rolling back to the airy in-and-out, and over a bright red fan jump that wasn't in the first course. We're hitting our distances, finding our stride, jumping like our lives depend on it. Because, maybe they do.

Finally, we're galloping full speed ahead at the water jump. Cyrus's ears are perked, his hooves barely touching the ground as we soar across the arena. Then, we're jumping over the water jump and I'm giving him a full extension, all the rein he needs to make it over this last obstacle. We hit the ground, go through the timers, and the stadium erupts into overpowering cheers.

I can barely hear the announcer's voice as he declares Cyrus and I the winners of the Lugano Diamonds Grand Prix. I fall on Cyrus's neck, hugging him and crying.

Elation washes over me and I'm sinking into the euphoria of the moment. I can barely stay in the saddle as Cyrus and I do a victory lap around the ring a few minutes later, Cyrus with a blue ribbon on his bridle.

We have the obligatory pictures—including one where I'm holding a check that's bigger than me—and a few with the second and third place riders. They congratulate me, and I almost forget how to say, 'thank you,' because I am cheesing so hard.

At long last, I'm able to return to my family, and it feels so good to be hugged and squeezed and fawned over by them. Anya is crying happy tears, and my mom keeps wiping her eyes and nose with tissues she's pulling out of who-knows-where. My dad looks perfectly at ease in this setting, with his Ralph Lauren clothes, Ray Ban sunglasses, and suntanned skin.

Monica keeps saying, "I can't believe you did that," and waving her hands in her face like she's hot.

My dad hugs me tightly to him and kisses the top of my head three times. "That was wonderful, Milochka." And I feel a swell of pride and sheer joy as I embrace him back.

"Maybe we'll sponsor a jump next season," he says, almost to himself as he surveys the International Arena. He turns back to the family, and announces that he got us a table at the Polo Club to celebrate.

Alex, Monica and Trina join us for the meal, and the excitement at the table can hardly be contained as we relive the Grand Prix over and over again. My cheeks are hurting from smiling so much, and Alex keeps looking at me like *his* cheeks are going to fall off, too. I keep glancing around the table at all of my favorite people—my parents, Anya, Alex, Monica, Trina—all of them here, celebrating with me. It's the best feeling I've ever experienced and I want to capture it fully, hold it in my head and my heart forever. Even when I'm ninety years old and have dementia and I can't even remember my own name, I want to remember this right here.

It's not just that I won the Grand Prix—although that's a huge part of it. It's that I was so crippled by fear, but I didn't let fear win. Was I terrified? Yes. Did I throw up everything I'd eaten this morning? Yes. But I still did it. I conquered, and all of the people I care about the most were there to witness it. To support me. To love me through it, no matter what happened.

And *that*. That's everything.

I haven't seen my parents this happy in a long time, and it's this that makes me change the plans Alex and I had made beforehand. Right as my parents order dessert, I announce, "Alex and I are going to take Anya back to Trina's barn."

Everyone turns to look at me like I just said I'm joining the circus.

"We just ordered dessert," my dad says. "You *never* miss dessert."

"Are you feeling okay, honey?" my mom asks, sincerely concerned that I'm skipping out on dessert.

"I'm *fine*. More than fine. Just stuffed, and Alex and I need to do some things at the barn, we want Anya to come with us."

"Horse people stuff," Monica says helpfully.

"It'll bore you," I insist. "You guys stay for dessert, and you can meet us at the barn when you're done."

Anya catches my eye and I wink at her. She sees right through what I'm doing, and seemingly so does Alex, because he's backing me up. Before my parents can argue, Alex is pushing Anya's wheelchair out of the restaurant; Trina and Monica are trailing us even though I'm certain Mon wanted dessert.

"You're so bad, *sestra*," Anya teases when we're back in the parking lot.

"What? Forcing my parents on a date? I thought that made me *good*."

"Oh, you're good," Monica says, "but we'll see if *they* are after this." She waggles a finger toward the restaurant.

I stick my hands in my pockets and shrug. Honestly, I know I can't control whether they make it through their alone time in one piece or not. But I am grateful to be able to do this next part of the plan sans parentals. Because I'm not sure they'd like it.

"I want to get you on a horse," I tell Anya once we get to the barn.

She gives me a strange look, one I can't totally decipher, before she says, "You do know I'm incapable of holding myself up, right?"

"Just wait one second."

"I won't move," she calls after me.

I come back from the tack room with the special saddle Alex and I ordered a few weeks ago. It has an attachment that functions as a back and neck support with straps to hold Anya onto the saddle. I explain to her how it works, and I anticipated having to cajole her into it, but when I'm done she says, "Okay" with her Anya-eye-shrug.

Alex gets Riker, an insanely calm lesson horse of Trina's, tacked up, and then comes the hard part—getting Anya in the saddle. I'll admit, it's not pretty. I'm shoving at her hip while Alex is tugging at her arm and then we recruit Carlos, who's propping Anya up from behind.

Anya, of course, is making droll comments through it all.

"Don't mind me," she says. "I'll just be hanging right here" as her head lolls over my shoulder.

"Maybe we should rent a crane, it would certainly be faster."

And—my personal favorite—her repeatedly and dramatically yelling, "Ow!" at Alex whenever he grabbed her legs. The first few times, he'd let go, startled, and she'd grin at him like a mischievous toddler.

"Am I making this difficult for you guys?" she says in her saccharine voice.

I'm thinking of a comeback that has something to do with the Ben and Jerry's she pounded last night, but Alex responds, "We're going to do whatever it takes to get you on this horse." And my heart swells, even as I'm sweating and shoving at Anya's waist, because this man is amazing. And he's mine.

It takes some adjusting to get it right, but eventually she's strapped in and we're ready to go. Carlos leads Riker around the field while Alex and I hold Anya onto the saddle. She can't steer, but we still put the reins in her hands, curling her fingers around them.

I was a little nervous Anya would think this was lame, especially since she was such a competitive, accomplished rider before. But if the smile splitting her face in half is any indication, she's having the time of her life. We walk them around the field several times, and then decide to venture out onto the trails. Riker is such a steady horse, I'm thankful we have someone I can entrust Anya with. And knowing Alex is just on the other side makes me feel completely at ease.

We're walking and talking and laughing when suddenly, Anya shrieks. And my heart plummets. Because maybe I was naïve to think this was a good idea.

"What? What's wrong?"

"Mila, look," she says, but I don't know where to look. I'm glancing around like a lunatic trying to figure out what's wrong, but then she says, "Look at my finger."

I look at her hands, and at first I don't see anything, but then, it happens.

Her pinky moves. Just barely. It tightens on the rein, then loosens. Then tightens again.

"Anya...are you doing that? Are you moving your finger on purpose?" I ask, because I need to be sure.

She nods, and there's tears streaming down her face. And then there's tears falling down my cheeks, too. And we're crying and laughing and taking videos of it and even Alex has tears in his eyes.

By the time we get back to the barn, I'm feeling so unbearably happy that I'm not sure my body can contain it all. We get Anya off the horse and sit her back in her wheelchair—which is no small task, but Alex handles it like a pro. I push Anya's wheelchair up to one of the tack trunks, and Alex and I take a seat next to her.

"What do you think this means?" I ask Anya.

"Honestly, I don't totally know." She's watching her pinky bend and flex again, and it's like watching Lazarus rise from the dead. "But I'm wondering if I had let mom do my exercises, I might've regained movement a lot sooner."

I nod, unsure of what to say. Because, yes, she should've been doing her exercises and going to physical therapy. But also, I get it. I've been unable to move on for so long, too. It's easy to look back and have regrets; it's a lot harder to actually learn from those regrets.

"What matters is that you're moving now," Alex says, because of course he has the right thing to say. He's Alex. I smile and squeeze his hand and he's smiling back at me and I have to consciously remind myself that Anya is right there.

I force myself to look away from his perfect-for-me eyes and take a deep breath. "Hey, so, I've been thinking," I start to say.

"Uh oh," Alex quips, and I smack his arm.

"I have a business idea, for the three of us."

Anya's eyebrow arches, and I notice this time, it's not quite plucked the way it normally is, and something about that makes me smile because maybe that means my mom is taking what I said to heart.

208 TIFFANY NOELLE CHACON

"I'm listening," she says, and I smile, because I can't wait to tell them all the crazy dreams and plans I've written down in my journal the past few weeks.

After I've told them everything, Anya says, "Well, obviously after today"—she curls her pinky again—"I'm in. Although I think we'll need a better system for getting people on the horses."

We all laugh and shake our heads, because it's true. That part was *rough*.

"I think it's a fantastic idea, Mila," Alex says with a twinkle in his eyes.

"Actually, it's your idea."

Alex looks confused. "I never..."

"I saw it on your list of business ideas. You know the note you showed me on your phone? I just kind of ran with it."

He smiles. "I like that."

"Thanks to my win today, we'll have some money to start with, but we'll need some pretty big investors to make it work." I look between Alex and Anya, and both of them are nodding.

"Well," Anya says, "it's a good thing I know just the investor."

# Chapter Nineteen

# Take the World

I'm fidgeting in a leather seat on the 18th floor of a Miami high-rise, waiting. I'm wearing the custom tailored suit my dad got me when I got to college. It's a tame navy blue, but I've paired it with a coral blouse that has a super fun necktie that I've formed into a bow. My hair is in a bun, paired with modest makeup. I'm ready for the boardroom. I glance beside me and grab Anya's hand, and she actually squeezes back, and it's the best feeling in the world.

Well, almost.

Because then I look over at Alex and fall into those gravitous dark brown eyes of his. He smiles at me, and it's like he's just released a whole cage of butterflies in my stomach.

On the way here, we jammed out to Sia's "Unstoppable," but now that we're here, I'm feeling very, well, stoppable.

"You don't look nervous," I whisper to him.

"Why would I be?"

"What if they laugh at us? What if they turn us down—"

"Mila, Anya," a voice calls from the far edge of the waiting area. "Mr. Caballero, they're ready for you." The secretary smiles at us as Alex pushes Anya's wheelchair down the hall toward the boardroom. I trail behind them, not entirely convinced I'm not about to throw up my morning smoothie all over my Jimmy Choos.

Before we walk into the room, Alex puts an arm around my waist and says, "No one could say no to you."

I roll my eyes. "Why do you say that?"

"Personal experience." And he winks at me before pushing Anya into the boardroom.

The boardroom is expansive and screams, 'I've got more money than the Queen of England,' with its polished walnut table and the midcentury modern leather seats and the abstract art paneling two of the walls. The other two walls are floor-to-ceiling windows showcasing the breathtaking ocean view.

My dad gets up from his seat at the head of the table and kisses my cheek, then Anya's. He shakes Alex's hand and introduces him to his partners, whom we've met on many years' worth of Fourth of July yacht parties. Mattia De Luca is short and squat, especially in comparison to my dad's tall, lean stature. He's balding and sweating through his Valentino three-piece suit, but I can tell that regardless of how much he sweats through his suits, he's the kind of guy to keep wearing them no matter what.

Osuke Hajime is the calm one of the group—the eye in the middle of my dad and De Luca's storm. When he shakes my hand with his perfectly manicured one, I'm amazed by how soft and pillowy his skin is.

At long last, it's time for us to present. With shaking hands, I connect my laptop to the drop-down screen and pull up our presentation. It feels a little like we're on *Shark Tank*, except thankfully without the cameras. I'm sweating, and suddenly very grateful my dad convinced me to choose a navy suit instead of a light-colored one where sweat would show through.

"As you know," Anya begins, "a little over a year ago, I experienced an incomplete C4 spinal cord injury after an accident with my horse. I was paralyzed from the base of my neck down, that is, until Mila and Alex decided to get me back onto a horse a few months ago."

I pull up a picture of Anya riding Riker, with Alex and I holding her in place.

"The personal benefits I've received from being back in the saddle are innumerable. Not only has my mental health improved, but I've actually started to have sensation and movement return slowly into my upper extremities."

"And Anya is not the only one who experiences these types of improvements after equine-assisted therapy," Alex says as I pull up a list of research studies done on the benefits of equine therapy. "The physical improvements are astounding, even for those whose paralysis is complete and permanent. Being on horseback helps improve muscle tone of muscles that the rider cannot even physically use. It helps with core strengthening, balance and fine motor skills, as well as improves mental health, helps them to build confidence and self-esteem, and improves their coping skills."

"What we'd like to create is a facility where paraplegics can come to rehabilitate—both physically and mentally," I say. "We would create a place where they can find refuge in these amazing, compassionate animals."

"What if someone is too scared to get on a horse? I hear what you're saying, but not everyone is as brave as you guys," says Mr. De Luca, and he's looking at us like we're absolutely nuts for getting on a horse in the first place. Which, maybe we are.

"There are still tons of benefits from being on the ground with the horses instead of on them. It's emotional therapy," I say, and I glance at Anya to back me up.

"It's true—just being around the horses, petting them or grooming them, releases endorphins. Which, I gotta tell you, after trauma, some endorphins are *really* nice to have around."

A chuckle goes around the table, and hope seems to take flight like a swan rising in my chest. They seem like they're really considering this, or at least hearing us out fully. I worry that they're just humoring us because we're dad's kids, and once we ask for money, they'll pat us on the head and send us on our way.

"Take us through some of the logistics," my dad says. Always the practical one. I take a deep breath, steeling myself for whatever might come once we tell them our budget.

"Well, first, we'd need a facility." I show several pictures of equine properties for sale throughout the tri-county area that would fit our needs. "We would also need special equipment." I show pictures of custom designed saddles, ramps for wheelchairs, special wheelchairs that can navigate the bumpy terrain of a barn, and, of course, horses. I pull up a spreadsheet with our budget. "We have seed money of $250,000"—the exact amount I won in the Lugano Grand Prix—"but we're aiming to raise $2.5 million, and then we'll ask the bank for another $2.5."

"Our goal is to eventually offer a full-service therapeutic facility," Alex says, "where it's not just the horses. We'll have therapists on staff and even social workers who can help our patients navigate this difficult time of transition in their lives."

The three partners are nodding, and I reach under the table and grab both Alex and Anya's hands. My heart is hammering and I have to remind myself to breathe. Because, this is it. All our hopes and dreams hang on this one decision.

"Well," Mr. De Luca says, "as you know, ViaTech deals mainly in the technological space. But we've been looking for a non-profit project we can put our name on. To be honest, I thought it would look more like teaching coding to kids in Liberty City." He chuckles to himself. "But I like this idea, a lot. And obviously there's the personal connection." He waves a hand at my dad and Anya. "What do you think, Osuke?"

Mr. Hajime has been the quietest throughout our presentation. He's asked the fewest questions, only picking at our budget a bit. He's very hard to read, and for a moment I think this is where our dream ends. But then, a wide smile breaks across his face and he says, "I love it."

"Give us a few minutes to discuss," my dad says, and we shuffle out of the boardroom. Once we're in the hallway, and the boardroom doors are closed, Anya and I give a little squeal and I wrap my arms around her head, and Alex is hugging us both, and we're laughing and talking over each other and it's exhilarating.

"New goal: get De Luca on a horse."

I laugh. "Good luck with that, *sestra*."

A few minutes later, all of our excited chatter dies away, and we're stuck waiting in the hallway, clenching our hands together.

"What do you think is taking them so long?" Anya asks. "It's a yes or no, right?"

I shake my head. "Maybe one of them doesn't like it and they just didn't want to say it to our faces."

After what feels like an eternity, my dad pokes his head out of the door. "You can come back in now." He's not smiling, and my stomach drops.

We go back into the boardroom and take our seats, Anya in her wheelchair beside me. My dad sits and clears his throat. The tension in the boardroom is so thick, you could cut it with a pair of blunt toddler scissors.

"Well," Mr. De Luca says gruffly, "you had a very compelling presentation, but we decided not to give you the amount you requested."

It feels like someone just dropped my heart off the roof of the high rise, and it's plummeting into the ocean below. *Here comes the head patting,* I think.

Then he breaks out into a smile and says, "We're going to give you more."

"What?"

"We're going to give you the full five million dollars."

I can't help it, my jaw drops. Beside me, there are tears falling down Anya's cheeks.

"Congratulations, you three," Mr. Hajime says. And that seems to break the spell, because we all start laughing and cheering and hugging each other. My dad comes around the table and embraces Anya and me, kissing our cheeks.

"I'm proud of you both," he says, and this brings tears to my eyes, too. "And you, too, Mr. Caballero." He gives Alex a slap on the back, and Alex gives him a modest smile in return, but I know he's thrilled.

Mr. De Luca pages my dad's new—and decidedly less friendly—secretary to bring a bottle of champagne, and soon we're toasting to our new business venture: the ViaTech Center for Equine-Assisted Therapy.

Later that night, after a celebratory dinner at N by NAOE on Brickell, Alex and I are sitting on my patio with the flames of the electric fire pit flickering in the dark. I'm curled up on the couch beside him, his arm around me as Alex's playlist murmurs over the patio speakers. And I can honestly say I've never been happier. I'm not old Mila, I'm not even the Mila of this past year, but I'm a brand new Mila who's learned from the past and made it my own.

"I wanted to tell you something," Alex says in that gentle way of his.

"Hm?"

"You inspired me to do something."

I sit up and face him, tucking my toes under his legs to keep them warm. "What's that?"

"I changed my major."

"To what?"

He gives me his bashful half-smile, and I'm wondering if he's nervous to tell me.

"I changed it to psychology. I thought that maybe..." he trails off, and I realize he *is* nervous.

I reach out and take his hand in mine, squeezing it. "Tell me what you want to say."

"You and Anya both have the business side down, for the Center, but I thought my focus could be on the therapeutic side. I didn't want to mention anything with your dad and the other partners until I talked to you but—"

"Alex," I cut him off, cupping his face in my hands. "That is the best idea ever."

"You think so?"

"I *know* so." I kiss him lightly on his nose, his cheeks, and then on his lips. And, can I just say I'm *so* glad we're past the point in our relationship where I keep shocking him with kisses? "You know," I say, "you'll get a salary with the Center so you won't have to work at the barn anymore. We all will."

"Really? I didn't even think of that."

"And..." I smile at him. "I may or may not have gotten you full insurance benefits that your mom can be on, too."

"Wait, are you serious?"

I nod proudly. "This is the part where you tell me I'm the best."

"You *are* the best," he says in a Nacho Libre impersonation.

I laugh and thread my fingers through his. "That's one reason why they gave us the extra funds, so we can all work exclusively on this."

"And school?"

"Yeah, I mean, this *is* my dad we're talking about. It's always *'and school.'*"

He exhales deeply, glancing up at the starry sky. "Wow, this is all really amazing."

"You're going to make an amazing therapist."

He smiles, and I love the way the flames are dancing in his dark brown eyes. He leans into me and kisses me again, soft and slow. "Just not your therapist," he says.

"That's true." I laugh and shake my head. "But why not my therapist?"

"I think it's kind of like being in the friend zone, just in a different way. I don't want to be friend-zoned, or, y'know, therapist-zoned." He laughs, his smile sparking across his face more readily than I've ever seen it. "Speaking of which, how was your appointment yesterday?" he asks, referring to my meeting with a new therapist, Gwen.

"It was really good. We're working on some breathing and relaxation techniques. It's actually been helping me fall asleep way faster."

"That's really good news, although I'll miss you texting me in the middle of the night when you can't sleep."

"Well, I'm not *completely* cured yet," I say with a sly smile.

"What a relief," he jokes, putting his forehead against mine. Then, he adds, "I'm proud of you, Mila. I know this hasn't been easy for you."

"No, it hasn't been, but now that I've found the right one, I keep thinking, why didn't I do this sooner?"

He shrugs. "You weren't ready, and that's okay. You're ready now and that's what matters."

I nod, because he's right. No point in looking back, since we can't change that. Now is the time to change the future.

"So," I say, "if you're not my therapist, what do you want to be?"

He thinks for a second and then says, "Your boyfriend?"

"Is that a question?"

"No," he says after he kisses me again. "It's a statement of fact." Then he's grabbing my hand and tugging me onto the patio to dance with him as Johnnyswim's "Take the World" comes on the patio speakers. I put my head on his chest and we dance as Abner Ramirez of Johnnyswim sings about being able to face anything together.

His hands on my waist and his chest beneath my cheek make me feel more alive than anything I've ever experienced before. Like I can take the world. With Alex.

I don't know what tomorrow will bring—they haven't even set a court date for Alex, though Ann assures us he shouldn't be deported—but I know that I have all that I want right here. And much, much more.

We'll take whatever comes at us, together.

"This might be my second favorite thing in the whole world," he says as he spins me, then pulls me back against him.

"Second?"

"I thought the first would be obvious," he says as he leans down to kiss me, and I stand on tiptoe to meet him. I'm sure my heart is going to burst if I'm even one iota happier.

"Well, *boyfriend*," I say as I look up at him, "you're also about to become my business partner. Are you sure you're ready for that?"

"I've never been more ready for anything in my life."

And then I tangle my fingers in his hair, pull him in for another kiss to tell him, *me too.*

END BOOK ONE

# Chapter Twenty

Keep reading for scenes from Alex's perspective...

# Chapter Twenty-One

# ALEX

I 'm lost in my thoughts, cleaning Amber's bridle—which she clearly hadn't done herself since last season—when Mila dashes into the temporary barn like she's on fire.

"I'm on in about twenty," she says, and my heart is pounding and my mouth is dry because I didn't see her coming, and I normally do. Her hair is down, her soft waves dancing around her face. *Get it together, man.* My hands are sticky with saddle soap so I wipe them on a rag and turn to get Cyrus.

"Got it, boss." I can tell she doesn't like it when I call her that, but it's a habit I got into when I knew I needed to keep my distance from her. When she started dating Michael. We're not friends, I'm not someone she'd ever consider. So 'boss' is my way of reminding myself of that I'm here to do a job, not find a girlfriend.

I busy myself with getting Cyrus ready, but I'm frustratingly conscious of Mila as she pulls her hair back and gets her helmet on. It's been years of torture, ever since she first came to the barn. But that Mila—so full of life, quick with a joke and a smile, so vivacious in every way—that Mila wouldn't give me the time of day. Why would she? What would life-of-the-party Mila have to do with me, nose-in-the-book *groom*? It seemed like a match made in equine heaven when Michael showed up. Even I couldn't deny that, as much as I wanted to.

But now, since Anya's accident, she hasn't been the same. And of course, Michael being who he is, he couldn't handle that. It breaks my heart to see her walking around like she's fractured into a million pieces. Every part of me wants to pick up those fragments and put her back together. I know it's not my job, it's not my place, but it doesn't stop me from wanting.

She's done adjusting her hair, and now we're silently tacking up Cyrus. She's chewing on her lip and I can feel the nerves coming off of her in waves.

"You nervous?" I ask like the idiot that I am. Of course she's nervous. She doesn't want to die—or worse, end up like Anya. And here I am asking her about it because I just want to talk to her, to say something. Because I'm a glutton for punishment.

She shrugs, trying to make it seem like she's not as scared as she really is. But I get it, I've been there. Terrified to get in my car, gripping the steering wheel with sweating hands as I get on the highway. Remembering my dad's twisted body, all of his limbs out of place, never to return back to their rightful places. I understand her in a way she'll probably never guess. "It's power and speed, which for whatever reason I don't like. I prefer to regroup before the jump off—assuming I get there at all. And, I don't know, the jumps always look the biggest the first week of WEF."

I want to hold her, to tell her it'll be alright, to give her all of the faith that I have in her. But instead, I just smile and tell her, "You'll do great."

And then, something strange happens. Mila looks at me like she's seeing me for the very first time. Really looks at me. And with that simple look, she's knocking down all the walls I've built up over the years, and hope bursts through. I take in her soft hazel eyes, her adorably tiny knob of a nose, the shimmer of makeup on her cheekbones, the way her full lips part as if she's about to say something.

Cyrus, the dirty little traitor, snorts loudly, and the spell is seemingly broken. But the hope is still there, swelling in my chest. It's only been a few weeks since she and Michael broke up, but I begin to wonder: if I asked her out, would she say yes?

I pass her Cyrus's girth, and she mutters to him as he blows out his belly like he always does. I take off his halter, and something compels me to whisper to Cyrus, "Take care of my Mila. Be good to her"—in Spanish, of course, so Mila doesn't know what I'm saying. Cyrus and I seem to have an understanding between us, and I trust he'll do as I say.

"Bewitching my horse?" Mila jokes, and the look in her eyes makes me want to do backflips. *Is she flirting with me?* I want to bask in what this feels like—to have Mila giving me her full attention, and perhaps even a little adoration. The hope inside of me is growing, and I don't know whether to tamp it down, or release it.

"A little hex to help you through to the speed." I give her a wink, something I would normally never be confident enough to do—and I see it. The moment when she distances herself from me. She glances away, and gives a little shake of her head. And I grab onto that hope that was trying to make a grand exit, and I shove it down as hard as I can.

I hand her the reins. "I'll give you a leg up."

There's a commotion a couple aisles away, and I hear one of the grooms from another stable shout out an alert: "INMAGRACIÓN! POLICÍA!"

The warning cry jolts through me, and I'm suddenly trying to remember what my dad told me to do all those years ago if I run into Immigration. I'm struggling with the wisps of a memory—do I run? Do I give them my fake ID that my cousin gave me almost a decade ago?

My first instinct is to run—my whole body is preparing for it, I can feel the urge in the balls of my feet—but then I turn and look at Mila. How could she ever look at me with any sort of respect if I run right now?

But then I think about my mom. I can't let them arrest me. She'll be alone and, with her health, it won't be long before she's either in a bad way here, or back in Cuba where she won't be able to get the medical care she needs.

I *have* to run.

There's more shouting in the aisles around us, police yelling and demanding to see identification. Out of the corner of my eye, I see a man running away from the barns, and an Immigration officer tackles him.

Mila is saying something to me, but I can't hear her. She grabs my hand and I look at her again.

"Alex?

"Immigration police," I tell her, the words forming slowly. I'm gripping her hand, my only lifeline. "If they arrest me, they'll send me back to Cuba. My mom will be here alone. She's...sick."

Why I'm telling her all of this, I don't know. Except that she's staring at me expectantly. Like she cares about what happens to me. And that just makes this so much worse. If she weren't looking at me like that, I could run and try to care less about how that makes me look.

"I'll help," she says, and my heart just shatters. How much more pathetic can I get? She's fumbling in her backpack, grabs something, and hands it to me. I look down. Her keys. To a BMW. Of course Mila drives a fifty thousand dollar car. "Get out of here."

As much as I appreciate Mila trying to save me, I know I can't take her up on this. What would they do if they caught me driving away in a car that's not my own? A *very* nice car that is clearly not mine? "They'll think I'm stealing your car. It'll just make it worse."

Her face falls, and even though *I'm* the one about to be arrested, I want to tell her it'll be okay. Even though it most definitely will not be.

"Right, okay. I'll drive, you can get in the backseat. Hide." She looks around, her eyes landing on a scrim sheet. "We can cover you with this. C'mon." She ties up Cyrus and grabs my hand, pulling me out of the barn. My thoughts have never been so jumbled—her plan isn't going to work, this is a total embarrassment, how in the world can I get out of this? What will Mila think of me once this is all over?

But I don't have time to process any of it, because the moment we emerge from the grooming stall, immigration is barging down our aisle. I have no choice but to run in the other direction, but instead Mila is tugging me back into the stall. I'm wondering if she thinks we're going to hide behind Cyrus when she whips off her helmet, throws her arms around me, and kisses me.

I have no idea what is going on, and at first I pull away, even though every part of me wants to lean into it.

"Trust me," she whispers. And her words, her lips against mine, her body so close to mine, it has my mind going blank and my body on fire.

For all the times I thought about this—Mila in my arms, lips on mine—I never could've imagined it would feel this good. Sure, the circumstances aren't exactly what I pictured, but there's no denying how right this feels.

I always knew Mila was beautiful, funny, talented. But the two of us together like this—we are electricity. We are fire. And I am consumed.

There are moments in your life when everything changes. And sometimes you know, and sometimes you don't. You figure it out after the fact. When we came here from Cuba, I was too young to know how it would affect my life. But when my dad died, I knew right away it would be life changing.

This. Kissing Mila, even in the midst of all this chaos. I know deep in my chest that this is one of those life altering moments. Something you look back on and say, *Yeah, that was it. That changed it all.*

And maybe that's what makes me open up, to kiss her more deeply, to show her just a glimpse of what's really in my heart.

"Immigration! Show your IDs," a man shouts from the aisle behind us. Every muscle in my body tenses, and I can't help but pause the kiss. This is it, I realize. This is the end.

At least I got to kiss Mila.

But Mila tightens her arms around me and murmurs, "Don't stop." A thrill goes down my spine at her words, but still, it's hard to keep kissing her when I know Immigration is about to grab me and arrest me out of her arms.

What a way to go out.

But this girl is not giving up—she fists my shirt in her hands and pulls me closer. And with that tiny movement, I have no breath in my lungs. There is nothing left in this whole world except Mila. Only Mila.

I step even closer until there's not an inch between us and run my fingers through her hair. I want her to know how I feel, how my very soul aches for her. I don't even notice when the Immigration officers give up and walk away. I can't tell if I've been kissing her for an eternity or only a few minutes. Despite the intense desire to keep kissing her forever, I pull away. But not all the way. I rest my head on her forehead, feeling her breath on my lips.

"It worked," she says. And for some reason, it's devastating. It's certainly not how I would sum up what just happened. What *did* just happen?

Magic? Lightning? Wildfire?

And all she can say is, *It worked?*

I shake my head as I lean an arm on the stall wall above Mila's head. I'm not ready to step away from her, especially because I know this might be the last time I'm ever this close to her. But I can't help it, I want to be near her. I want to hold her, to tell her that this right here is better than my wildest dream. But I know I can't.

So, I back away. "I can't believe it," I say truthfully. "Thank you for...that." Because how do you sum *that* up?

I'm sorely tempted to build my walls back up, to never let hope out again. I can't look at Mila for fear that she's looking at me with disdain.

"We need to get you out of here, before they circle back," Mila says.

"You'll miss your ride."

"There will always be another one." Her eyes meet mine, and I can feel hope peeking out from behind the shattered walls of my heart. Mila cares. And right now, that's enough for me.

Or, maybe it's not. I realize it suddenly—I want her to love me, I want her to want me the way that I want her. And I'm not going to sit around and wait for that to happen.

Not anymore.

# Chapter Twenty-Two

# ALEX

I wake up slowly, to the feel of Mila's lips on my cheek. And I've never had an experience like this, where a dream has been fulfilled that I never even knew I had. All I know is that I've wanted this, to wake up to Mila's kiss, without really knowing it.

My arm, which I wrapped around her waist last night to keep her from falling off the tack trunk, is still encircling her, and I give her a squeeze, hugging her to me just a little before letting go. "I, uh, thought you were going to fall over last night." And then I reluctantly pull my arm away.

She's quiet this morning, almost shy, and it's so unlike Mila and yet, I love it. I want to kiss this quiet Mila, to tuck her in my arms and be silent with her. Instead I say, "I'm sorry I should've taken you home earlier. I tried to wake you a few times, but you were out. As in, I checked your breathing a few times," which isn't *exactly* true.

When Mila fell asleep, I ran a tentative finger across her perfect cheekbone to see if she would wake up, and she didn't. She *did*, however, threaten to topple over the side of the tack trunk, so I happily put my arm around her to keep her in place. And I just sat there for what seemed like hours, listening to her breathe, soaking in this moment of being with Mila.

At one point, she shifted so that her head was on my chest, her knees tossed over my legs. It took every ounce of self-control for me to not run a hand down her smooth legs. In fact, I *sat* on my hand to prevent me from doing just that. Of course, it didn't stop me from admiring them at such a close distance.

She was beautiful, that was for certain. But it wasn't just her beauty that had me up in the middle of the night, distracting her from her anxiety and feeding her so she wouldn't pass out the next day. It was her spirit, her goodness, her passion. And even though she felt like those things had dwindled this past year since Anya's accident, I was seeing them more clearly than ever. Especially now that she was letting me get closer to her.

"I guess that spinach worked," she laughs, and her nose crinkles as she does and I want to kiss it. "Honestly, any sleep last night is a win for me."

"That's kind of what I thought, too," I tell her as I look for any excuse to touch her again. She has a strand of hair falling in her face, so I reach out and tuck it behind her ear. I can tell she's holding her breath as my fingers brush the side of her neck just below her ear. There's a warmth spreading through my chest, and I'm sure she feels it, too. I'm wondering if she'll let me kiss her, when suddenly the spell is broken and she's darting up, looking down the breezeway.

I glance over my shoulder to find Michael. Which is just dandy. And of course he has the audacity to look upset at seeing us together—it makes me want to remind him that *he* broke up with Mila. He has no right to any sort of jealousy here.

But then I look over at Mila, who is looking guilty and confused. Why exactly that is, I can't say. But all the warmth I'd been feeling freezes over faster than a Siberian winter.

"Hey, uh, shouldn't you guys be at the showgrounds?" Michael asks, looking between me and Mila.

"I, um..." Mila's floundering. And honestly a part of me is okay with her grasping right now because I want to know how she would synthesize last night.

But, since I am who I am and I'd do anything for Mila—even if it means helping her save face in front of her lousy ex-boyfriend—I say,

"She couldn't sleep last night, so she came to the barn and fell asleep on the tack trunk."

"I see," Michael says, though he's obviously blind because he broke up with Mila. "Well, I'm just switching out my bit. I'll see you tonight, Mila?"

*Que?*

I look at Mila, hoping against all hope Michael got it wrong and they're not hanging out tonight, but she just says, "Yep," and Michael smiles at her and leaves. I'm not the violent type, but I definitely want to break this guy's perfectly straight teeth.

My whole body tenses, and I'm ready to run, ready to just get out of here and leave everything behind. I'm pouring my heart out to this girl, and this is what I get? She's getting back with *him*?

"Thanks for, um, everything," she says as she stares at the ground.

*Coward.* I want to say, but I don't. Too scared to leave the safety of a pissant like Michael. "Happy to help, boss," I say instead, throwing out that name like a shield. She winces, but I don't care. How can I, when she's repeatedly shown she doesn't really care about me? And yet I just keep trying. Like a fool.

I stand up and start to walk away, until I realize I brought her here.

"I brought you—"

"You're my ride—"

"Right," I say, grabbing my keys. "Let's get you to Trina's."

We drive in silence and I'm thankful Trina's is so close. I consider asking her why she's doing this. Why she's hanging out with me in the middle of the night, falling asleep in my arms, and then the next minute acting like nothing happened. Planning to get dinner with Michael. A date? Is it a *date*?

I tighten my hands on the steering wheel, wishing for just one second it was Michael's neck instead.

Why can't I find the words to ask her about this? To get to the truth of what's going on between us? When it comes to me, the answer startles me: I don't want to know. I'd prefer to live in this tense limbo where it feels like Mila's falling for me than face the truth that she's stringing me along.

So, even though I should ask her what the deal is, I don't. I can't. And that's on me.

She gets out of the car, flinging a paltry *See ya* at me as she exits. As I drive back home, I try to convince myself to back away. I adore Mila—I have for years—but I can't let her stomp all over my heart. I won't have anything left of it by the time she decides who to choose.

Later, I tack up Cyrus, and I visualize building a wall around my heart to protect it from Mila. It's an exercise my therapist taught me when it became apparent I was too easily affected by what other people thought of me, though I'm not sure my therapist would approve of me using it in this way.

By the time I get Cyrus to the schooling ring of the International Arena, I'm calm. I won't let Mila break my heart. I won't let her use me to get Michael back. I won't go down in flames just because this seemingly unattainable girl is batting her eyes at me.

Gorgeous, unmatched hazel eyes.

I groan. This is going to be harder than I thought, and I've already endured years of agony.

But then I see her, crouching at the fence of the schooling ring, puking her guts out, and in one millisecond, my walls are gone and my heart is going out to her. I jog to her, tugging Cyrus along, and rub her back as she throws up all the food I gave her last night. When she's done, I hand her my water. She takes a few sips, and I help her stand on shaky legs.

"Well, now that that's done, I think that means you're ready," I tell her with my best attempt at a smile. She moans and leans her head on my chest. I want to wrap my arms around her, to hold her, but instead I pour a little cold water in my palm and rub it on her neck, a trick my dad taught me to cool your body temperature faster.

It's in tiny moments like this that it hits me—hard—how much I miss my dad. He would know exactly what to say, precisely what to do, if he were in my situation. So I just try to think of what my dad might do if he were me.

"Mila?"

"Uh huh?"

"I know you feel like crap right now, but think about how epic this will be once you win this thing. Or at least get around the course in one piece. It'll be a story you tell your kids and grandkids until they're bleeding from their ears."

She laughs, which is a good sign, and then she gives me a hard time about my pep talk, which is an even better sign. And it's then that I realize how much of a goner I am. Because no matter how terrible I felt a second ago, when Mila smiles, my whole soul lights up.

I get her on Cyrus and she warms up. The two of them look fantastic, like they can read each other's minds. And maybe they can.

We're waiting at the in-gate when it happens. Another accident on course, the rider right in front of Mila takes a rotational fall, landing horrifically, and can't get back up.

I can feel Mila panicking beside me as the ambulance drives into the ring. Her face is more pale than I've ever seen it. I reach out and grab her leg, squeezing it to show her I'm here. I don't know what to do, don't know what to say, but I'm here.

When it's finally time for her to go in, Trina says, "You don't have to," which I know is the wrong thing to say. If Mila doesn't go now, she might never try again. I'm still holding on to her leg, trying to channel every ounce of faith I have into her. She can do this; I know she can.

After a moment, Mila says, "Can I just have some water?"

I hand her my water bottle and she downs a few sips and hands it back. I squeeze her hand as my fingers brush over hers when I take the bottle from her. She's looking at me, and I can tell she's as scared as she's ever been. I give her leg another squeeze, and then, she's bending down, grabbing my shirt and pulling me into a kiss. I'm so shocked I barely kiss her back, barely get a brush of her lips against mine, before she's off into the ring.

It's an odd juxtaposition how you can feel so empty and so full at the same time. As Mila rides away from me, I feel the emptiness of her departure. The blank space where her lips just were. But there's a fullness, too. She didn't *have* to kiss me. She wasn't saving me, there was no good reason for it except she wanted to. I don't totally understand the timing of it—is she afraid something is going to happen to her and she's kissing me goodbye? But whatever her reasoning, I accept it.

And it devastates me.

Because this girl has a power over me I never intended anyone to have. With one word, she can break me. With one smile, she rebuilds me. And with one kiss, she utterly destroys me.

# Chapter Twenty-Three

# ALEX

I'm on the bottom bunk, staring up at the slats in the bed above mine. I don't know what to call this room I'm in—it's not quite a cell, not quite a bedroom. There are two bunk beds and a bathroom. Faded carpet and a loud window AC unit. There's a man snoring in the top bunk, I haven't met him yet. He's been asleep since I got here. Beside me, on the other side of the room, there's another man sprawled across his bed, doing Sudoku. He's wearing an orange jumpsuit, just like me.

He must finish the puzzle he's working on, because he smacks his lips and closes his book.

"Whatchu do, cuz?" he asks me.

"Nothing, man."

"Right. We're all here cuz of nothing."

"Some of us are."

"Aye, aye, aye. You gonna be like that, huh?"

I roll onto my side and prop myself up on my elbow. Guess this guy wants to talk. I suppose it's better to make friends than enemies, so I ask him, "What are you here for?"

"Same old, same old."

"So you've been here before?"

He smiles at me and the wrinkles on his pudgy, bald head deepen. "Something like that."

"Is there a way out?"

"You mean, like escape?"

"No, I mean, how do you keep from being deported?"

"Thought you'd never ask, cuz."

Manny—that's his name—launches into an hour-long explanation of how his cousin's husband's uncle can get me a birth certificate of some dead American that will magically solve all my problems.

"I'm not into that kind of thing," I tell him cautiously.

"Oh, so what are you into? Getting deported?"

"I'd rather get deported than do something illegal."

"News flash, cuz, you *is* illegal."

I shake my head. He's right, but also, he's so wrong.

"Look, man, for fifty K, you can go home. Be free. Get your life back."

"What makes you think I have that much money?"

"People come up with money when they desperate. Don't you gotta a girl or a uncle or somebody that can throw you a bone?"

My heart twinges when he says *a girl*, and then I'm thinking about Mila again. How it felt for her to be truly mine, if only for a few hours. And how painful—how completely and utterly torturous—it was for all of that to be ripped away. And of course it's my fault, of course I could see that she wasn't over Michael yet and I still pushed it. Still pushed her.

A chill goes through me, and I get it now. I get why people swear off love or just stay casual in their relationships. This burns like nothing I've ever experienced. And I know if I had just kept all that hope locked away, it wouldn't be this bad.

"You there, man?" And I realize Manny's been talking to me and I haven't been paying attention. "You thinking about your girl, huh?"

Before I can stop myself, I say, "She's not my girl."

"Ah, I see."

And for some reason, at Manny's beckoning, I tell him everything. How I loved Mila for so long. How she kissed me to save me from ICE. How we danced around each other these past few weeks until finally—finally—she chose me. Only, she didn't. Not really. I tell him everything, and I say it as nonchalantly as I can, even though I'm weeping on the inside.

When I finish, Manny whistles. "Bro, you got it all wrong."

"Huh?"

"She loves you, man."

I grunt, unable to voice my disagreement.

"You said she was there, with your mama, when you called her? After you got arrested?"

"Yeah."

"Chicks don't stick around like that unless they really feelin' you. Trust me, I know."

"But the whole thing with the picture, and then she's all wrapped up in her ex literally hours after she kisses me—"

"Yeah, but was she kissing *him*?"

"Well, no."

"See. There you go."

"It's not that simple."

"It sounds to me like it is."

"She was with him for two years."

"Yeah but she's not with him right now, is she? She's sitting around waiting for your sorry butt to come home. But guess what? You ain't going home unless you buy your way out."

I roll my eyes. "Manny, let me be straight with you: I'm not going to buy your dead cousin's brother's husband's birth certificate. And then what? Be indebted to whatever gang hooked that up for you?"

He laughs, a booming laugh that startles the snoring man above me. "Who says I'm in a gang?"

I fix him with a stare, and then he laughs again. "You think you smart, huh, kid?"

"Not smart enough to stay out of here, apparently."

"No, that's true. And dumb enough to lose the girl you love."

"Thanks, man."

We settle back into our respective beds, and I'm thinking about what he said. It's true that Mila was with my mom, hours after I got arrested. If she was back with Michael, or if she were done with me, she wouldn't have done that. At first I thought it was out of guilt that she stuck around, but maybe it was that she really does care? And Manny is right, it's not like they were kissing. Maybe I should've heard her out.

But of course now it's too late. I'll probably never see Mila again. And that thought alone cuts me deeper than anything else.

"You're a good kid," Manny says after a while. "Stick with me and I'll take care of you."

I glance over at him, wondering what his protection will cost me, but he's back to his Sudoku. A moment later, one of the guards bursts into our room. He's tall and chubby, with steel toe boots. And I wonder if he's ever kicked anyone with them.

"Mr. Caballero?"

"Yeah?"

"Your lawyer's here."

I follow the guard down the hallway, even though I know I don't have a lawyer and this must be a mistake. But I resolved not to make any ripples when I came here, to stay under the radar and just get out of here as fast as I could. Even if that meant going to Cuba faster, at least I wouldn't be locked away, unable to help my mom.

The guard leads me to a conference room, where a woman in a maroon suit and wire-rimmed glasses smiles at me.

"Are you Alex?" she asks.

"Yes, ma'am."

"I'm Ann Lopez, your immigration attorney. Mr. Kozak sent me."

It takes me a moment to understand what she's saying—it wasn't a mistake. Mila's dad sent her to help me. Which means Manny was right. Maybe she doesn't love me, but she certainly cares. She hasn't forgotten about me.

My hands are shaking as I take a seat across from Ann. I'm trying to listen to what she's saying, but all I can think is: Mila cares. She really cares.

Ann and I talk for hours, and when she leaves, I'm starting to believe that I just might be able to get out of this mess. I don't know how it's possible, and honestly, I'm scared to believe it at all, but Ann seems positive she can help me. So I hold on to that since it's all I have.

When I get out of my meeting with Ann, it's recreation time. I join in a game of basketball with Manny and some of the other guys. It feels good to move after days of being cooped up in a cell and soon I'm sweating freely.

After the game, Manny is talking with some of the other guys, and it seems like he's trying to sell them the same thing he tried to sell me. I shake my head as I down a bottle of water. What an interesting guy, I think. He simultaneously gives me love advice and tries to sell me a dead person's birth certificate. Who *does* that? But for some reason I like him.

A guard appears beside me, the same one with the steel toe boots. I glance up at him, but he doesn't make eye contact with me. He's watching Manny and the other guys, and then he turns to look at me and his glare is so full of disdain, I almost topple off the bench. How can someone hate me without ever knowing me? But it's so clear to me that this guy does.

And then, he spits. It lands right on the top of my sneaker and I've never felt more hated in my life. I can't very well tell this guy off—he's already in a position to kick my guts out— so I just swallow and turn away, ignoring him as if he didn't just spit at me.

He laughs, like he got me. Which, he did. And I wonder just what kind of person gets pleasure out of this? The answer comes to my mind immediately: someone without love.

And that's when I decide I'm going to give Mila a chance. I don't know what our future looks like, I don't know if I'll ever get out of here, but at the very least, I'm going to hear her out. She deserves that much. *We* deserve that much.

The next day, Ann shows up and tells me I'm going home. I have so many questions, so many things I want to know, but I'm also so overcome with gratitude that I pull her into a hug. At first, she's taken aback, but then she pats my back and squeezes me.

"Thank you, Ann."

"Well don't thank me, I'm just doing my job. You can thank Mr. Kozak when he gets here."

"Mr. Kozak?"

"Yes, he said he'd be here to take you home."

I swallow, trying to calm the nerves that are suddenly taking hold of me. I've never met Mr. Kozak before, but from the little I know from Trina and Mila, he's not to be trifled with. And now he's essentially picking me up from jail? What will I even say to him on the car ride home?

Ann walks with me to the front desk, where I hand them the sheet of paper with all of my personal items listed on it. The female guard at the desk looks it over and passes me a bag with my things.

"There's a bathroom around the corner if you want to get changed before Mr. Kozak gets here," Ann tells me, and I'm relieved that at the very least I don't have to go home in this prison uniform.

I hurry to the bathroom, turning on my phone as I go. I scroll through my missed texts until I land on one from Mila. It's a long, long thread and I don't know if I'm ready to read it now, or if I want to savor it later, when I'm not in the bathroom of a deportation center. But my impatience wins out and I lean against the bathroom counter as I read her text.

Mile: *Alex, when we first went to Kickback at the start of the season, I was totally and completely unavailable. I was heartbroken, devastated by Michael, torn apart by Anya's accident. I was a shell of a person, not really living, just going through the motions. All I wanted was to win Michael back because that's what made me feel safe and secure. It was what was familiar and comfortable. Looking back, I see that it wasn't necessarily Michael I wanted back, but Old Mila.*

*But then you waltzed in, and little by little, you crumbled the walls around my heart that I didn't even know I had. And when those walls started to come down, I started to heal for the first time since Anya's accident. I finally came alive for the first time.*

*But it's painful, and scary, coming back to life. I still thought the goal was to be Old Mila, when in reality I'm never going to be that girl again. And I'm starting to see that's not a bad thing. Sure, there's pain and a lot of heartache that come along with being New Mila, but I'm seeing that sometimes those things mold you into a better version. A more compassionate, more selfless, more real person. And that's all because of you, Alex. You and me, together.*

*I can't define yet what we have, but there's an electricity and a realness with you that I've never experienced with anyone else. So even though all I wanted was to win back Michael, you won me over. After he came over for dinner (the night of those Insta pics), it was clear that I was so close to my goal of getting back together with him, and then I realized I didn't even want that anymore. I just wanted you. And this whole time I was fooling myself thinking that I wanted something that wasn't even right for me.*

*Alex, I still want you. When you saw me hugging Michael the other day, it was because I told him we were definitely over. It was a goodbye hug. And not just goodbye to Michael, but goodbye to Old Mila. You made me see that I don't even want to be her anymore. I want to be me. New Mila. And New Mila chooses you. And even though you pushed me away these past few days, I still choose you. I'll be waiting for you, Alex, no matter where you are or how long it takes to find our way back to each other. I know that as sure as I draw breath and my heart beats (albeit a little erratically at times), we are supposed to be together. Don't give up on us, Alex. Please.*

I read through the text several times, making sure my mind is understanding what my heart already knows.

Mila wants me.

*Me.*

Not some smooth-talking, life-of-the-party, Baywatch-wannabe, rich kid. I can't take her on helicopter rides or rent a yacht or drive her around in an Audi.

But I can love her like no one else ever has.

And I was really close to messing it all up. The reality hits me like a two-by-four over the head and I have to grip the bathroom counter to keep standing.

I have to remind myself: I'm getting out of here. I'll make it right with Mila. And I'll never, ever let her go.

I quickly change, wash my hands and face, and then hurry out to the foyer where I find Ann standing with a man who looks intimidating enough to be Mr. Kozak.

"You must be Alex," he says, and shakes my hand. He has Mila's eyes—or, I suppose *she* has *his* eyes. Except his are dark and cold in a way hers have never looked. At least not to me.

"Yes, sir. I'm very grateful for your help."

"I'm doing this for Mila." He quirks an eyebrow at me as if to say, *You better not screw this up.*

*Loud and clear*, I want to say. "Yes, sir."

"She obviously cares about you," he says, glancing over me from head to foot, "though I can't be sure yet why that is."

"I guess we'll find out soon enough," I say truthfully.

Ann is saying something about a court date, but I can't quite pay attention because there she is. Mila is running through the parking lot, like a blur of light, and I watch as she pauses outside of the doors, indecision clouding her face. Is she regretting coming here? Sending me that text?

But then, she walks through the front door and our eyes meet, and that's all I need. Before I know it, she's in my arms. I don't even care right now that her dad is here, or Ann. All that matters is that Mila is here, and that Mila *wants* to be here. I hold her to me, trying to telepathically convey everything I feel in this moment. But it's not enough. I'll always want more.

She steps away before I'm ready, and I let go reluctantly. But when I see her face, her eyes looking up at me—wondering, questioning how I feel about her—I just want to throw her over my shoulder and get her out of here. Alone.

She kisses her dad and shakes Ann's hand, and it's clear they've talked a few times and I'm more than curious to know the whole story. Then, before I can blink, Ann and Mr. Kozak are saying goodbye and heading into the parking lot. Mila takes my hand and leads me toward her car. The whole thing is so surreal; I just narrowly escaped getting deported and here I am, the only thing I can think of is that this beautiful girl is holding my hand.

We get to her car, but I'm not ready for seat belts and consoles to separate us, so I pull her into a hug. Having her here, in my arms, with this electric current running through us, connecting us in the supernatural way that it does, it has me wondering, does every couple experience this? Or is this unique? 'Chemistry' doesn't even come close to describing what's between us. It's divine.

"Thank you," I tell her, because she's saved me yet again. "You didn't have to do all this for me—"

She pulls away, and the separation is physically painful. I want to reach out, to bring her back to me, where she belongs. But she's got her hands on her hips and she's looking at me like she's about to chastise me. "Yes, I did, Alex. I don't want to lose you; I just found you."

"Can I tell you something?" I say, pulling her against my chest. "You've had me for a long time."

Her perfect lips twist into a small smile. "What do you mean?"

I run a finger along her jawline, counting three tiny freckles along the way. I want to kiss each one of them. "Maybe one day I'll tell you." I breathe a sigh of relief, and there's a million things I want to say, a thousand secrets I want to tell her. But I start with, "I'm sorry I wasn't willing to hear you out about Michael. The whole thing really threw me for a loop, and with those pictures he posted, I just thought..."

"I know what you thought, but I think Michael was doing that on purpose. He's not a bad guy, but I think he was trying to mark his territory."

"I can see that now." I sigh again and rub a hand over my face. It's hard to fathom how things have changed so quickly over and over again the last several days. And yet here I am, with the girl of my dreams. And I'm not dreaming. It's real life. And I can't believe it. "One of my roommates, this guy named Manny, he kind of helped me reason it out."

"Sounds like a smart guy."

"He also offered to get me a U.S. birth certificate off a dead guy for fifty thousand dollars."

"So he's an outside the box thinker, I like that."

I smile at her and shake my head. I can't stand to be separated from her a second longer, so I take her hand and tug her to me, and it feels like all the stars in the universe have just aligned. "I read your text," I tell her because I want to know for certain if she really meant those things.

"Yeah?" She throws her arms around my neck, and I know in that instant that she really did mean it all. "What did you think?"

"I think I want to kiss you," I say honestly.

She laughs and tilts her head up to me. "I've been waiting a long time for *you* to kiss *me*."

"Then I won't keep you waiting any longer." I press my lips against hers, and savor the softness of her lips, the feel of her curves against me, the way she smells of summertime.

The hope that had been threatening to burst through my walls—it's gone. Replaced by the reality of this girl who cares enough about me to save me, to stand by me, to believe in me. I don't need hope anymore, because I have what I've always hoped for right here in my arms.

My Mila. My love.

*Order the next book in the series, FALL: Order FALL on Amazon*
*Keep reading for the first chapter of FALL!*
*Want to connect? I have a Facebook reader group where I give updates,*
*let you vote on things like character names and book cover designs, and*
*post teasers and bonus content! Join here:*

**ORDER FALL**

Scan the QR code or go
to the link below to
purchase the next book
in the series:

tinyurl.com/orderfall

# Download a Sneak Peek of Equestrian Dreams #2

*Keep reading for the first chapter of FALL, or download the first THREE chapters using the QR code below:*

**JUMP #2: FALL**

Scan the QR code or go to the link below to download the first few chapters of the next book in the series: FALL.

tinyurl.com/fallthenovel

# First Chapter of FALL

I press my heels into the gelding's sides and feel a thrill as he surges forward over the grassy field. We're galloping as one, unsure where I begin and he ends. I knot my reins, resting them on his neck as I extend my arms out like I'm flying. And maybe I am.

It's one of those perfect Florida fall days where the sky is bluer than it has any right to be, the air is crisp and breezy, and the scent of hay carries all the way to the field. I take a deep breath as the wind whips past me, and it's as if I'm both bigger and smaller than I really am. Being out here, I feel like I'm part of something *more*—all of my atoms are connected to every other atom in this universe. I am expansive, vast. And somehow that makes me feel small, too. I can sense the enormity of the cosmos thrumming through me—a girl on her horse—and I'm content to just *be*.

I pull up the gelding, a chestnut horse named Harley, and look around at the ViaTech Center for Equine-Assisted Therapy. I can't hold back my smile. We made this place, and it is perfection. The centerpiece of the property is a wood-paneled barn with a gabled roof and charming dormers. The barn has an overhang held up by wooden pillars that gives it a look akin to a wraparound porch. Behind the barn, there are several grassy paddocks and two round pens. Harley and I are at the front of the farm, which has a wide-open field next to a covered ring. The roof of the covered arena is aluminum, and on rainy days when the raindrops ping off the metal, it's my favorite sound in the world.

The back of the property is where Alex and Mrs. Caballero live. It's an adorable little house, with white paneled walls and a black gabled roof to match the aesthetic of the barn. Alex put in carriage lights and flower boxes under the windows with pink petunias for his mom, which led to us dubbing it "The Cottage."

Beside the barn is a wheelchair ramp that allows us to help our patients onto horseback more easily. As we walk back to the barn, a bay mare with long eyelashes named Jasmine, or Jazzy for short, pokes her head out of the stall, a low rumble in her throat. At first, I think the whinny is for me, and then Alex walks up and I realize Jazzy, like every other horse in the world, has a keen Alex radar. Of course he has treats in his pockets that he offers to Jazz. My heart squeezes at the sight of this man in my favorite place in the world—a place we created together.

"Good morning, Mila Kozak," Alex says, pulling me into a hug. I wrap my arms around him and snuggle into his chest as he kisses the top of my head. I wonder if this will ever get old, the feeling of Alex's solid chest beneath my cheek, his heart beating in time with mine. The way he says my name, like it's the most cherished phrase he's ever spoken.

"Good morning." I stand on tiptoe and kiss him briefly. If I had my druthers, it would be for *much* longer, but we have a busy day ahead of us and Anya is wheeling around the corner like her chair's on fire. Anya's straight, dark brown hair is flowing around her shoulders, her sky-blue eyes sparking with energy. A wheelchair cannot dampen my sister's raw beauty—even in the middle of the barn, she looks like she could be on a shoot for Vogue, with her sky-high cheekbones and naturally tinted lips.

The other thing that the wheelchair can't dampen in Anya: her razor-sharp focus.

"Break it up, children," she says with a wave of her hand—a gesture that still sends a thrill through me because a year ago, Anya couldn't move her hand at all. Anya's incredible recovery of movement in her arms is a constant reminder of why we're doing what we're doing at the Center. Coming here is an act of hope. A hope farm, if you will. "We've got a new patient coming in twenty."

Alex and I break apart, sharing a laugh because Anya rarely tolerates displays of affection—or anything she would consider a distraction. Being *unprofessional* is the ultimate insult.

"Tomás ready for the intake?" Alex asks as Harley nuzzles him for treats.

"He actually showed up on time today, unlike someone." Anya gives me a very pointed look.

"I was up super late finishing one of those lame online discussions for my International Finance class," I tell her. I'm in my penultimate semester of my online MBA program at the University of Florida, and I have to say, I'm so ready to be done with it. Now that the Center is up and running, trying to juggle grad school, my Center responsibilities, *and* competing on Cyrus—it's a tad much. Of course I'm not going to get much sympathy from my sister, because she's been doing pretty much the same thing (minus competing), except she graduated last semester at the top of her class.

Show-off.

Dad wanted us to 'diversify' our education, so Anya got her MBA from the University of Southern California—she claims she identifies as a California girl after her Stanford undergrad experience. I was thrilled to get into UF, though my dad's top choice was Indiana. I got waitlisted there and ultimately never heard back from them, but it's honestly for the best because I love being a Gator.

I untack Harley and put him in his stall, where he takes a deep drink from the automatic waterer in the corner. Most mornings, I exercise one or two of the horses before the day begins so that they're calm for our patients. Harley might get ridden a couple times today, but only at a walk, so we're both doing each other a favor by having a morning gallop. I stroke his neck and give his cheek a kiss, then head to the lounge area in the center of the barn.

It's a small but comfortable room with wood floors and sparse but cozy seating—most of our clientele are in wheelchairs so we don't need a ton of seats. There's a well-used coffee bar in a cute teal cart beside a stocked mini fridge and a side table with various brochures scattered across it. We recently put up a peg board with pictures of our patients with the horses and some notes and cards that people have written to us. Evenly spaced across the wall are pictures of horses, including one of Cyrus and me that Alex put up when we first built the barn.

Connected to the lounge are two offices—one for one-on-one therapy appointments and the other for Anya, Alex, and me to use when we actually get to sit down and do paperwork or answer emails. Occasionally we use it to complete our schoolwork if there's a lull in the day.

I make a cup of coffee for Anya and then myself, dumping in sugar and flavored creamer until it's practically white. Tomás, our only other full-time employee at the moment—the rest are volunteers or part-time, like our therapist—strolls into the lounge carrying a box of cinnamon streusel muffins. Tommy, as we affectionately call him, is Alex's younger cousin. He showed up at Alex's doorstep seemingly out of nowhere a few months ago, asking for a job. He didn't know much about horses, but he was a quick study and hardworking. He's basically our catchall employee—he helps with the horses, acts as an office assistant, and generally lends muscle when we need it. He's become an essential and pleasant part of our operation.

"Morning," he says, handing the box to Anya. She grabs a muffin, then hands me one and we touch muffins in a 'cheers' like we've done since we were kids.

"How you two don't have diabetes is beyond me," Alex says, shaking his head.

"Just wait thirty years," Tommy says with a coy smile.

"Don't worry, she'll drive him crazy before that," Anya cuts in. But Alex looks at me with a glimmer in his eyes that says he's not going anywhere. And just like that I'm feeling warm and tingly, not at all ready to work. It's been a year and a half of life with Alex, and each day is better than the one before it.

Tommy grabs a bottle of water and chugs it. I don't know anyone in the world with more energy than this guy. He's young and boyish looking, with jet-black hair and wide, brown eyes that I'm sure get him out of a lot of trouble. He walks on the balls of his feet like he's about to break into a sprint at any second, and he's always vibrating with energy and humor. In the months that he's been at the Center, I've come to adore him like the little brother I never had.

He grabs the new client paperwork and clipboard from the office. "Who should I get on the cross ties?"

"Well, let's chat with her first and see what she might need," I tell him, and Alex nods. When we first meet a new client, we like to get a sense of what they need, what their comfort level is with horses, and which of our six horses might be a good fit. Our newest volunteer, Ben, walks in to get himself a cup of coffee. He's a retired FBI agent, with the leathery brown skin of someone who's spent their retirement days outdoors. He's wearing a ViaTech hat to cover his bald head—he claims that for every day he worked in the Organized Crime division, he lost a hair. "After twenty-five years, it's shocking I have anything left," he'd told us.

Our barn cat, Gata, strolls into the lounge like she owns the place. Which, I suppose she does. Of course she goes straight to Alex, curling around his leg. Gata is our resident rat-catcher and she's proud of her prowess. She *does* keep the rats away in exchange for seemingly unending praise from Alex, who's currently speaking to her in Spanish with more affection than he speaks to me.

Anya fills Tommy and Ben in on the day's schedule and what their responsibilities will be. "We're expecting our new therapist, Luke Craig, today as well," she says. "Big day." Our previous therapist resigned after her maternity leave, so Alex had to scramble to find us a replacement while Anya and I were on our annual sister's trip. We haven't met him yet, but Alex has raved about him so much I can't imagine a better fit for the Center.

Anya and I eat our muffins and sip our coffee as the guys discuss a soccer match they watched last night. Anya and I pause, hovering over our coffee cups, when the barn begins to shake with resonating bass from outside. "What is that?" Anya snaps, and we all shuffle out of the barn to see a massive Ford F.350 Super Duty on wheels that might qualify as monster truck status. Blasting from the interior is "Hard Out Here For a Country Boy" by The Cadillac Three, the bass reverberating through my chest as the truck pulls up in front of us. The song cuts off just as the singer is elaborating how hard it is to drink cold beer and love a "hot girl." I glance over at Anya, who may as well have fire coming out of her ears.

"Alex, I swear, if that's our new therapist, I'm going to need a lobotomy," Anya says.

We're all holding our breath as the far side truck door opens, a ramp lowers to the ground, and a man in an aluminum manual wheelchair rolls around the back of the truck.

Our new therapist is wearing a snakeskin cowboy hat, a white button-down shirt with a bull's head bolo tie, jeans, and boots with silver tips. I expect to have to pick Anya's jaw off the ground, but that thing's clenched tighter than an alligator in a death roll.

"Should I schedule your lobotomy for Tuesday or Thursday?" I whisper to Anya.

Luke Craig rolls up to us, then tilts his hat and says, "Howdy, y'all." He's handsome in a quintessentially American boy kind of way, with blonde hair, blue eyes, and a smile that could be on a billboard. My first thought about Luke's appearance is that if he weren't decked out in the cowboy apparel, he'd be just Anya's type. "Didn't realize I had an audience. Would've turned the music up if I'd known," he says with a wink.

It's then that I notice his wheelchair is completely covered in all kinds of faded, peeling stickers. I squint to read one of them with a bucking bronco that says, "I do my own stunts." Yeah, definitely *not* Anya's type.

Anya turns to Alex, glaring flaming daggers at him before muttering, "I need a minute. Alone." And then she wheels off.

*Order the next book in the series, FALL, to see what happens with Luke and Anya! Order FALL on Amazon*

# Did you enjoy reading JUMP?

I'm on a mission to get 500 reviews of JUMP! Reviews are the lifeblood of books and authors. Please support this Indie author by reviewing the novel:

**REVIEW JUMP**

Scan the QR codes or go to the links below to review JUMP.

Goodreads:

Amazon:

https://tinyurl.com/ reviewGR

https://tinyurl.com/ JUMPamzn

# Acknowledgements

Thank you, God, for the written word, for love stories, for horses, and for making me a writer. And thank you for giving me the best love story ever as inspiration to write about young love.

Thank you to my husband, Tyler, who has supported me and believed in me even when there wasn't any good evidence I *should* be believed in. You laughed, gasped, and even cried through this book with me, and that makes it all worthwhile. Everyone always thinks that when I'm writing romance it's obviously about you — and even though I'd like to think I'm creative enough to not be autobiographical...it's all about you. You are my one, my only, my ever. The details are different, of course, but everything I write about love is because of my love for you.

To my boys, Finn and Justus, you fill my life with so much joy. Even if nothing comes of this book, my life is fulfilled because I get to be your mom.

To Mom and Dad, for supporting me, cheering me on, and being the best parents a girl could ask for. Oh, and thanks for all the horses and riding lessons. That helped, too.

To Amanda, my *sestra*, my ride-or-die, my Ultimate Beta Reader and Editor-in-Chief of all things Mommy of Mayhem and beyond. Your belief in me and this book has powered me through some crippling self-doubt. Thank you for always having my back in literally everything.

For Andrea, my *sestra*, who helped me with all of the music-related terms for the final Grand Prix scene and who let me "steal" her daughter's name. Thank you for always rooting for me and reading my stuff even though you hate reading (don't worry, I won't tell anyone!).

To Kat Nics, editor extraordinaire, I'm so grateful for your feedback and investment in this book. You took this manuscript to another level.

To my entire family—my parents, Jeff and Lisa, Dorothy and Scotty, Joey and Philippa, Daniel, Kyle and Amanda, Ryan and Andrea—for being the best support system a writer could dream of. Thanks for putting up with my endless book-related texts in our family thread. Many, many thanks to my brother, Daniel, an extremely talented film-maker, who created an incredible book trailer that really should be a movie trailer. You have always believed in me, even more than I believe in myself, and that means the world to me. (If you haven't seen the book trailer for JUMP, check out the QR code on the next page. And you can also check out Daniel's Instagram to see his latest filmmaking projects.)

Shannon Vogt did an incredible job narrating the audiobook and she deserves all the props! I'm so glad I found you! Thanks for bringing my story to life in a way I could have only dreamed of.

Many, many thanks to Amber Shipp who swooped in to save the day. God knew I needed you!

Thank you, Rachel, for being a wonderful therapist and for being willing to give me feedback on the psychological aspects of Mila's character.

Thank you, Dani Williams, for taking my author photo and being an amazing, supportive friend!

Wayne Rodriguez, Florence Guerrier and my aunt, Deborah Stearns, provided valuable information about immigration and ICE detention facilities. Thank you!

I had some amazing professors at the University of Tampa MFA in Creative Writing program—Kevin Moffett, Jennifer Vanderbes, Mikhail Iossel, and Corinna Vallianatos. I am a better writer because of you. Thank you.

To all of our babysitters, without whom this book might never have been completed: Lauren, Rita, Emily. Thank you for loving my kids so much.

To Obi and Bug, the best horses in the world. It's because of you and my connections with you that made writing this book so easy.

To my incredible launch team who made marketing this book so fun and exciting. Thank you, thank you, thank you!

And to you, dear reader, for reading this book. I'm grateful you're on the ride with me.

*Want to connect? I have a Facebook reader group where I give updates, let you vote on things like character names and book cover designs, and post teasers and bonus content! Join here:*

**VIEW THE JUMP TRAILER HERE:**

Scan the QR code or go to the link below to see the JUMP trailer:

https://tinyurl.com/jumptrailer

## VIEW DANIEL'S FILMMAKING PROJECTS

Scan the QR code or go to
the link below:

https://tinyurl.com/danielfilms

# Follow Tiffany

Follow Tiffany

Sign up for Tiffany's monthly newsletter on her website, TiffanyNoelleChacon.com or scan the QR code below:

@tiffanynoellechacon

@tiffanynoellechacon

tiffanynoellechacon.com

# Discussion Questions

1. Have you ever had a goal or dream you're afraid to pursue? Have you faced your fear? Why or why not?

2. Were you surprised when Mila kissed Alex in chapter 2? What else could she have done to help him in that moment?

3. Why do you think Michael broke up with Mila? Does this make him a "bad" guy? Why or why not?

4. In chapter 6, Alex shares the idea of "radical acceptance" with Mila. How did the characters in the book come to a place of radical acceptance by the end of the novel? Is there anything in your life that you need to radically accept in order to move forward in a positive way?

5. In chapter 8, Alex said, "Sometimes you just have to borrow other people's faith in you." Have you ever borrowed someone's faith in you? Or lent your faith to someone in order to help them face a fear or overcome a challenge?

6. Was Mila wrong to want to change in order to win back Michael? Why or why not? Why do you think it was so hard for her to "let go" of Michael?

7. Was this truly a love triangle between Alex, Mila and Michael? Why or why not?

8. How did Anya's accident and paralysis affect her family? Why

do you think this "trickle down" effect of her accident is an important part of the story?

9. Why did Mila have such a hard time facing her sister after her accident? Have you ever had difficulty facing a challenging situation head–on?

10. When you read the scenes from Alex's perspective, was there anything that surprised you? How did it change your perception of Alex?

11. What were ways that Mila neglected her mental health throughout the novel? How did that change as the story progressed?

12. In chapter 15, Alex gifts Mila a journal in order to help her figure out what she wants to do with her life. Why do you think this was what finally prompted her to choose Alex?

13. Did you have a favorite character? To whom did you relate to most?

14. If you could give Mila advice at any point in the book, which part of the book would you choose? What would you say to her?

15. If JUMP were a movie, who would you cast as the actors/actresses?

*Author's note: I love book clubs and would love to support yours! If you would like me to send you Equestrian Dreams bookmarks, signed name plates, or if you'd like me to come speak at your book club, reach out to me at tiffany@jumpthenovel.com.*

Made in the USA
Monee, IL
19 November 2023

46926389R00155